iNTERACTIVE SCIENCE

For Inquiring Minds

Lower Secondary **VOLUME A**

Tho Lai Hoong
Tho Mun Yi
Josephine Fong
Consultant: **Dr Hoh Yin Kiong**

APPROVED BY MINISTRY OF EDUCATION
for use from 2008–2012

Marshall Cavendish
Education

Published by Marshall Cavendish Education

An imprint of Marshall Cavendish International (Singapore) Private Limited

Times Centre, 1 New Industrial Road, Singapore 536196

Customer Service Hotline: (65) 6411 0820

E-mail: tmesales@sg.marshallcavendish.com

Website: www.marshallcavendish.com/education

First published 2008

Reprinted 2008, 2009 (twice), 2010, 2011, 2012

ISBN 978-981-271-617-0

Printed in Singapore by Times Printers, www.timesprinters.com

Acknowledgements

The publisher is grateful to the following for granting permission to reproduce their photographs:

Abiomed, Inc. (page 153)

Andrei Tchernoy/ iStock International Inc. (page 147)

Department of Defense, Defense Visual Information Center, Riverside, CA (page 56)

Don Bayley/ iStock International Inc. (page 39)

DSC Clinic (page 227)

Jim DeLillo/ iStock International Inc. (page 215)

Kativ/ iStock International Inc. (page 147, 150, 192)

National Library Board (page 65)

Marshall Cavendish Benchmark, © 2007, Nuclear Power Plants (page 19)

Oliver Sun Kim/ iStock International Inc. (page 147)

Phil Morley / iStock International Inc. (page 135)

Philip Jose/ iStock International Inc. (page 137)

Photolibrary (page 47, 119, 132, 135, 137, 150, 189, 190, 192, 202, 213, 221, 227)

PUB (page 8, 103)

Reef0537, NOAA's Coral Kingdom Collection/ Dr. Dwayne Meadows, NOAA/NMFS/OPR (page 144)

Reef0557, NOAA's Coral Kingdom Collection/ Dr. Dwayne Meadows, NOAA/NMFS/OPR (page 144)

Reef0684, NOAA's Coral Kingdom Collection/ Commander William Harrigan, NOAA Corps/ Florida Keys National Marine Sanctuary (page 202)

SIMS Group UK Ltd (page 97)

Stephen Sweet/ iStock International Inc. (page 220)

Steve Geer/ iStock International Inc. (page 99)

The U.S. Geological Survey (page 174)

WHO (page 21)

Every effort has been made to trace the holders of copyright, but in some cases, without success. To these, the publisher offers its apologies, hoping that they will take its liberty in good faith. The publisher would appreciate any information that will enable it to acknowledge the copyright holders in future editions of this book.

Preface

This *Interactive Science – For Inquiring Minds* series is specially designed for lower secondary science students in the Express/Normal (Academic) stream. It comprises a textbook in two volumes, theory workbooks, practical workbooks, teacher's guides and teacher's editions of theory workbooks and practical workbooks.

Explanations of science concepts are illustrated in an interesting and easy to understand way. Authentic examples involving everyday situations are carefully chosen so that students can relate to them easily. Activities are designed to infuse information technology (IT), national education (NE), critical, creative and self-regulated thinking into the learning of science.

The textbook contains attractive and brilliant photographs and original illustrations to captivate students. The photographs are captioned to stimulate students either to relate the text to their own experiences and knowledge or to provoke them to think about the facts presented. Learning outcomes as outlined in the MOE Science Syllabus for E/N(A) stream are clearly stated at the beginning of each chapter.

Sections and questions which are optional for the Normal (Academic) course are marked with the icon .

These features in the textbook will help students understand the science lessons better:

- **Try This!** provides opportunities for students to make inquiries, share ideas and experiences and carry out cooperative learning.

- **Exploring Further** consists of questions or activities to encourage students to think further into a topic.

- **Science in Action** exposes students to the applications of science in daily life and in the industry.

- **Science Nugget** provides snippets of scientific knowledge which may not be in the syllabus, but are relevant, useful and interesting.

- **Workbook Link** links the concepts learnt in the textbook with the activities and practical experiments in the theory and practical workbooks.

- **Connect** shows the links between science and other fields of study.

- **NE** represents National Education and relates science to country.

- **Key Points** provides a summary of the important concepts and principles in the chapter to help students recall what they have just learnt.

- **Let's Review!** is included at the end of each chapter in the form of structured questions.

- **At a Glance** provides a graphic summary of the chapter in the form of a concept map.

- **Think Tank** consists of open-ended questions that develop and inculcate critical and creative thinking skills among students.

- **IT Links** shows students Internet resources they can access independently to further explore each topic.

This science series with its inquiry approach will make the learning of science at lower secondary level more interesting and exciting thus establishing a good foundation for further studies in upper secondary science.

About The Book

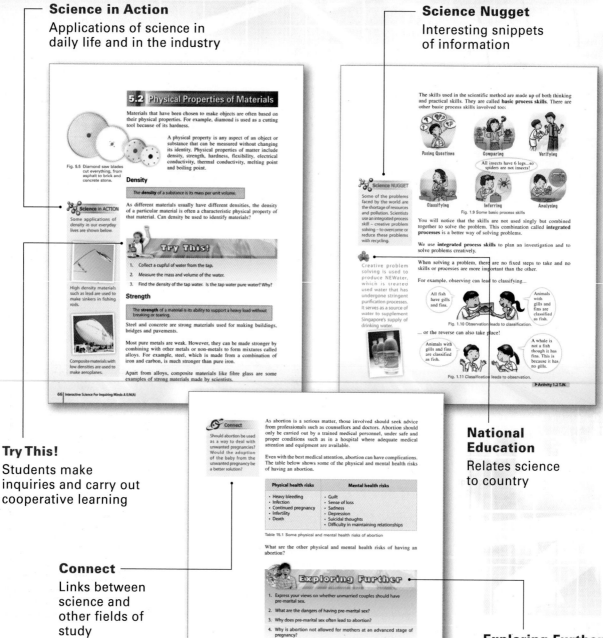

Science in Action
Applications of science in daily life and in the industry

Science Nugget
Interesting snippets of information

Try This!
Students make inquiries and carry out cooperative learning

National Education
Relates science to country

Connect
Links between science and other fields of study

Exploring Further
Questions or activities to encourage students to think further into the topic

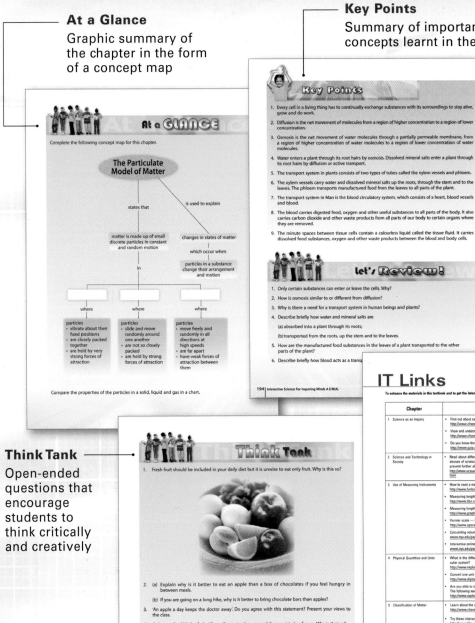

At a Glance

Graphic summary of the chapter in the form of a concept map

Key Points

Summary of important concepts learnt in the chapter

Let's Review!

Structured questions included at the end of the chapter

Think Tank

Open-ended questions that encourage students to think critically and creatively

Workbook Link

Links textbook concepts to activities in the theory and practical workbooks

IT Links

Students use Internet resources to further explore each topic

Contents

Theme 3: DIVERSITY

Theme 4: MODELS AND SYSTEMS

Science & Technology

Science Processes & Applications
- Science as an Inquiry
- Science and Technology in Society

• Overview •

Why study science?

Science provides a logical way of understanding the world around us. Scientists constantly learn more about the world, through observations and experiments.

Together with technology, science has a great effect on the human society and on the Earth itself. It can improve the quality of our lives, but if abused, it can also be harmful to us and our environment.

In this theme, we will examine the basics of scientific inquiry, as well as the benefits and limitations of science and technology in the world around us.

• Key Inquiry Questions •

- Why did this event, phenomenon or problem happen?
- What conclusions can I make based on my observations and evidence collected?

Science as an Inquiry

In this chapter, you will learn to:

• show an awareness that science is not confined to the laboratory but is manifested in all aspects of the world

• recognise that the study and practice of science involve three major elements:
    – attitudes
    – processes or methods
    – products

• use scientific inquiry skills such as posing questions, designing investigations, evaluating experiment results, communicating and learning

• show an appreciation that scientific inquiry requires attitudes such as curiosity, creativity, integrity, open-mindedness and perseverance

• recognise that the products of science are the tested data collected by scientists for centuries

• explain with examples how scientists have formulated concepts, principles and theories

• value individual effort and team work as part of scientific inquiry

How does science affect our daily life, the society and the environment?

Science is everywhere – you cannot miss it!

Just look at all the technology surrounding you now: washing machines, computers, or even a mobile phone. They are all based on scientific discoveries.

Fig. 1.1 Personal Digital Assistant (PDA)   Fig. 1.2 Mobile phone

The cosmetics that young women put on are also the result of science. The right amount of chemicals must produce the right types of colours and textures, and on top of that, they cannot irritate human skin!

Fig. 1.3 Cosmetics   Fig. 1.4 Tsunami

New discoveries can also help solve problems affecting the Earth, such as floods, pollution or even global warming. Early warnings of hurricanes or tsunamis can save countless lives, and that is because of the constant work of scientists.

Is science limited to the laboratory? Definitely not! It shows up in every corner of the world and affects the human society in many ways. We will learn more about how to study and practise it in the coming sections.

1.1 Science as an Inquiry

Science is studying nature in a logical manner and finding out how it affects us and the environment.

To study and practise science, you have to involve the following three major elements: **attitudes**, **processes** or **methods**, and **products** of science.

How do all the three elements come together in **scientific inquiry**?

We are by nature curious...

...so, we always ask questions...

...and try to find the answers using suitable skills.

What we learn will add to our knowledge ...

... or even make us ask more questions!

Will we stop being curious? Let's continue to find out!

Fig. 1.5 Science as an inquiry

Every new thing we learn in science or other areas in life will make us more curious and want to find out more. This becomes a learning cycle which keeps going on. Learning is a lifelong process!

▶Activity 1.1 T.W.

1.2 Attitudes in Science

Children are full of curiosity – they like to ask why-questions a lot! It is just our human nature to be curious about our environment. It is one of the **attitudes** required of all science students.

Besides curiosity, many other positive attitudes are also important in the learning and practicing of science.

Fig. 1.6 Attitudes in science

Try This!

1. In groups of four, discuss what the various attitudes described in this section mean to you. How would your behaviour change if you adopt each of these attitudes when faced with a problem?

2. Thomas Alva Edison was one of the greatest inventors in modern history. There are more than 1 000 inventions under his name!

   Read about his life in the following webpage and pick out the attitudes that made him a successful inventor:

   http://www.thomasedison.com

Thomas Edison

1.3 Processes or Methods in Science

We face problems every day and we usually use a systematic method to try and solve them. Let's look at one such problem:

Fig. 1.7 A typical method of solving problems

In experiments, scientists follow a scientific method that is systematic. It comprises mainly of the following steps:

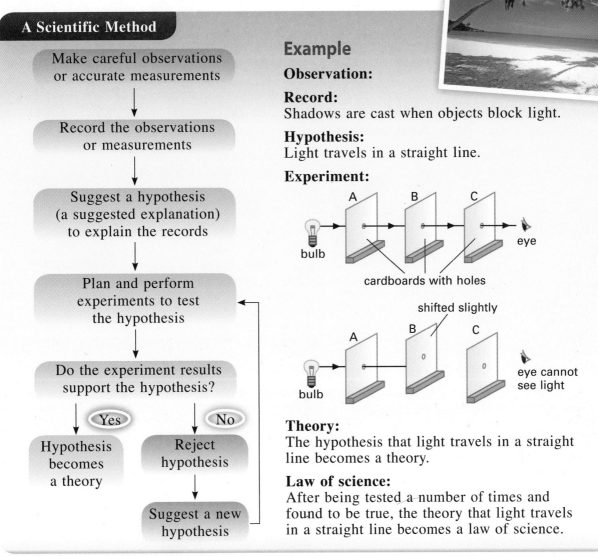

A Scientific Method

Make careful observations or accurate measurements

↓

Record the observations or measurements

↓

Suggest a hypothesis (a suggested explanation) to explain the records

↓

Plan and perform experiments to test the hypothesis

↓

Do the experiment results support the hypothesis?

Yes → Hypothesis becomes a theory

No → Reject hypothesis → Suggest a new hypothesis

Example

Observation:

Record:
Shadows are cast when objects block light.

Hypothesis:
Light travels in a straight line.

Experiment:

bulb
A   B   C
cardboards with holes
eye

shifted slightly
bulb
A   B   C
eye cannot see light

Theory:
The hypothesis that light travels in a straight line becomes a theory.

Law of science:
After being tested a number of times and found to be true, the theory that light travels in a straight line becomes a law of science.

Fig. 1.8 In what way is a scientific method similar to real life problem solving?

One of the important steps in the scientific method is the planning of the experiment. The planning of the experiment includes the following:

- identifying the fixed, independent and dependent variables in the experiment
- deciding on the apparatus needed
- taking safety procedures and precautions
- determining how to conduct the experiment and, collect and analyse the data

Science NUGGET

When we conduct an experiment, we investigate how one variable (independent) affects another (dependent).

To do this, we have to make sure that all other variables (fixed) are constant.

The skills used in the scientific method are made up of both thinking and practical skills. They are called **basic process skills**. There are other basic process skills involved too:

Posing Questions   **Comparing**   **Verifying**

All insects have 6 legs...so spiders are not insects!

Classifying   **Inferring**   **Analysing**

Fig. 1.9 Some basic process skills

You will notice that the skills are not used singly but combined together to solve the problem. This combination called **integrated processes** is a better way of solving problems.

We use **integrated process skills** to plan an investigation and to solve problems creatively.

When solving a problem, there are no fixed steps to take and no skills or processes are more important than the other.

For example, observing can lead to classifying...

All fish have gills and fins.

Animals with gills and fins are classified as fish.

Fig. 1.10 Observation leads to classification.

... or the reverse can also take place!

Animals with gills and fins are classified as fish.

A whale is not a fish though it has fins. This is because it has no gills.

Fig. 1.11 Classification leads to observation.

▶**Activity 1.2 T.W.**

Science NUGGET

Some of the problems faced by the world are the shortage of resources and pollution. Scientists use an integrated process skill – creative problem solving – to overcome or reduce these problems with recycling.

Creative problem solving is used to produce NEWater, which is treated used water that has undergone stringent purification processes. It serves as a source of water to supplement Singapore's supply of drinking water.

Laboratory Apparatus

Scientists use different types of apparatus to carry out experiments in laboratories. The apparatus enable the scientists to make accurate measurements and observations too. All laboratory apparatus should be drawn in outline and with correct proportions, as shown in Table 1.1 below.

Apparatus	Use	Apparatus	Use
Test tube	For containing or heating small amounts of substances	Boiling tube	For containing or heating/ boiling larger amounts of substances than the test tube
Beaker	For containing chemicals or collecting liquids	Conical flask	For containing chemicals or collecting liquids
Flat-bottomed flask	For containing chemicals when preparing gases if the process requires no heating	Round-bottomed flask	For preparation of gases if the process requires heating
Measuring cylinder	For measuring volume of a liquid to an accuracy of 1 cm^3	Burette	For measuring volume of a liquid to an accuracy of 0.1 cm^3
Pipette	For measuring very accurately a specific volume of liquid (e.g. 25.0 cm^3, 50.0 cm^3)	Thistle funnel	For transferring liquids into a flask

Apparatus	Use	Apparatus	Use
Filter funnel	For separating an insoluble solid from a liquid with the help of a piece of filter paper	Gas jar	For collecting gases
Bell jar	For separating an experiment setup from the outside environment	Evaporating dish	For evaporating a liquid from a solution
Crucible	For heating solids directly over a flame	Tripod stand	For supporting apparatus during heating
Water trough	For containing water when collecting gases	Displacement can	For displaced liquid to flow out through its spout

Apparatus	Use
Retort stand	For supporting apparatus during experiments

Table 1.1 Common laboratory apparatus

▶Activity 1-3 P.B.

1.4 Products of Science

Besides having the right attitudes and appropriate scientific skills and processes, you also need to know the **products** of science.

Products of science are...

- information such as results obtained from experiments
- ideas such as theories and laws

...that have been collected over time.

An example of a scientific law is Newton's law of gravitation, which describes how large bodies like planets interact with one another.

Scientists usually work on what others have discovered.

Sometimes, they will add on to the knowledge base, but at other times, totally new discoveries are made.

This is why it is not possible to have an unchanging product of science.

Try This!

Your teacher is going to show you a peeled apple that has been left in the open for an hour.

Can you explain what makes the flesh turn brown?

How can you test your explanation? Keep in mind the attitudes you must adopt when doing this activity!

What products of science can you use here? How can you obtain these products?

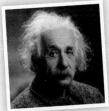

Key Points

1. Science is studying nature in a logical manner and finding out how it affects us and the environment.

2. The study and practice of science involve three major elements: attitudes, processes or methods, and products.

3. The scientific inquiry approach that involves the use of ethics and attitudes, skills and processes and products can be used effectively in the study and practice of science.

4. Attitudes adopted in scientific inquiry include creativity, integrity, objectivity, cooperating with others, responsibility, perseverance, open-mindedness and curiosity.

5. Skills used in scientific inquiry include observing, communicating, making a hypothesis, using apparatus and equipment, predicting, generating possibilities, elaborating, defining the problem, posing questions, comparing, verifying, classifying, inferring and analysing.

6. Processes used in scientific inquiry include planning investigation and creative problem solving.

7. Products of science are information such as results obtained from experiments and ideas such as theories and laws that have been collected over time.

Let's Review!

1. What is science?

2. Explain how technology - a result of scientific discoveries - can be seen in a hair salon and a supermarket.

3. Why is perseverance an important attitude required in most scientific inquiries?

4. Name a scientific inquiry skill used in writing a report on an experiment.

▶Revision 1 T.W.

At a GLANCE

Study the following concept map for this chapter.

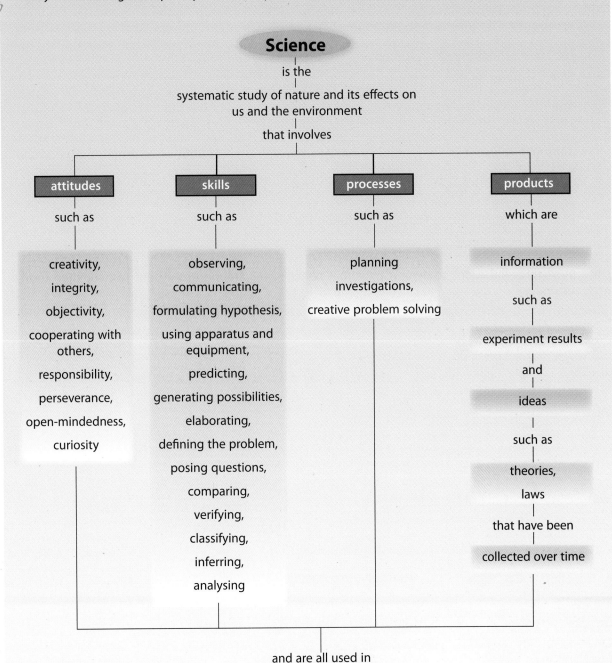

Science

is the

systematic study of nature and its effects on us and the environment

that involves

attitudes	skills	processes	products
such as	such as	such as	which are

attitudes — such as: creativity, integrity, objectivity, cooperating with others, responsibility, perseverance, open-mindedness, curiosity

skills — such as: observing, communicating, formulating hypothesis, using apparatus and equipment, predicting, generating possibilities, elaborating, defining the problem, posing questions, comparing, verifying, classifying, inferring, analysing

processes — such as: planning investigations, creative problem solving

products — which are: information

such as

experiment results

and

ideas

such as

theories, laws

that have been

collected over time

and are all used in

scientific Inquiry

1. Why is it important for the following people to have some basic knowledge of science?

   (a) An author writing a school textbook

   (b) A baker baking a cake

   (c) An architect designing a house

2. Scientific revolution happens when there is a great change in the products of science and their applications.

   Past revolution – Industrial Revolution freed us from the limits of our muscle power.

   Present revolution – Information Technology (IT) Revolution frees us from the limits of our brain power.

   Future revolution – Biotechnology Revolution will free us from the limits of life itself.

   Do you agree with the above statements?

3. State three situations to demonstrate that science is all around us and not just confined to the laboratory.

▶ **Portfolio Assessment 1 T.W.**

Science and Technology in Society

In this chapter, you will learn to:

- discuss the uses and benefits of science and technology to society

- show an appreciation of the moral and social issues in the applications of science

- show an awareness of the limitations of science and technology in solving societal problems

- evaluate the benefits and limitations of science and technology

- communicate your ideas on the benefits and limitations of science through discussions and presentations

- value individual effort and teamwork as part of scientific inquiry

In what ways has the invention of man-made satellites affected the way we live and interact?

Since ancient times, we have been applying our scientific knowledge to benefit our society using technology. Now, it can be found in almost every part of our lives.

Fig. 2.1 Paper is a product of technology.

For example, what you are holding now is a product of a 2 000-year-old technology – paper!

Fig. 2.2 A typical laboratory

Take a look at your classroom or laboratory. Can you spot ancient technology among the modern ones?

Technology can definitely improve our lives. However, when abused, it can also cause problems in the society such as war and pollution.

Fig. 2.3 War

In this chapter, we will look into the uses and benefits of science and technology and how they can solve problems in our society, up to a certain limit.

2.1 Uses and Benefits of Science and Technology

Fig. 2.4 A typical hawker centre

Go on a mini-field trip to a hawker centre (such as the one shown in Fig. 2.4) with three or four of your classmates. You may want to look into and around some stalls. You can ask yourself or even interview the stall vendors using the following questions:

- What three objects that make use of technology (products of technology) are found in a hawker centre?
- How are they being used?
- If they were not present, how would it affect the:
  - vendors' working conditions;
  - customers taking the meals?

You will realise that technology helps to improve the lives of many, including that of the stall vendors.

Technology is the application of scientific knowledge for the use and benefit of mankind.

Not only does it enable us to lead an easier and more comfortable life, it can also improve our health.

Look at the following products of technology. Can you describe the ways in which they have benefited us?

Computer

Calculator

MRT train

Man-made satellite

Clothing

Bicycle

Fig. 2.5 Products of technology – can you describe their benefits?

Flavr Savr is a type of genetically-modified (GM) tomato. The tomato has an extra gene added to it to delay rotting. This is actually good news for the farmers.

However, the idea of eating unnatural tomatoes is still debatable. Some people think that eating GM food will cause health problems. What health problems do you think people are afraid of?

Fig. 2.6 Genetically-modified tomatoes

▶**Activity 2 T.W.**　　▶**Activity 4 P.B.**

Fig. 2.7 Dolly is the world's first cloned mammal.

Cloning is another example of technology that brings up a lot of debate. Cloning is like making a baby who is your twin.

Cloning animals may lead to the cloning of humans. In fact, human embryos have already been cloned in laboratories. Can you think of some diseases that this type of cloning can cure?

If the cloning of humans is possible, a lot of moral questions are up for debate. What moral concerns do the public have about human cloning? With your class, discuss the following questions concerning cloning of humans and decide whether they are right or wrong.

Right or Wrong?

- Should human cloning be allowed so that couples, especially the childless ones can have babies?

- Should parents be allowed to choose the sex, height, eye colour, intelligence and other qualities of their child?

- Who owns the right to clone a person – the scientist who discovered human cloning or the person himself?

- Is it right to make changes to the qualities of humans?

- Is it right to create new life?

- Should people be tested in advance to see if they will get a genetic disease?

2.2 Abuses of Science and Technology

Although scientific discoveries benefit society, they can cause problems too. Let's take the invention of dynamite as an example.

Dynamite was invented by a Swedish scientist named Alfred Nobel. It was supposed to be used as a safe explosive for mining and construction.

However, dynamite became a tool for destruction in war.

Fig. 2.8 Alfred Nobel

There are many other problems caused by the abuse of technology. Pollution is one such example in the modern world.

Fig. 2.9 Smoke emitted from vehicles

Fig. 2.10 Waste water produced by a chemical factory

Can you think of other problems?

Abuses in technology have a lot to do with the choices people make. It is important to make a choice that will cause minimal harm to society and our natural environment.

Science NUGGET

Nuclear power station

The invention of nuclear power can solve the world's energy shortage problem. However, if abused, it can also mean the start of a disastrous nuclear war.

Atomic bomb explosion

Exploring Further

Imagine that your family wants to get a car and has to decide between the following:

- a large car which has a powerful engine but emits a lot of harmful gases, or

- a small car which has an efficient engine and gives out less harmful gases

Which car would your family choose? What is your decision based on?

2.3 Science and Technology – Their Limitations

While science and technology can make our lives better, they also have their limitations – they cannot solve *all* our problems.

Fig. 2.11 Volcanic eruption   Fig. 2.12 Tornado

Can our current science & technology stop natural disasters completely?

To date, science and technology have failed to solve societal problems dealing with emotions and failed relationships between people.

The problems involving emotions of people and their complex relationships are studied by a psychologist.

Fig. 2.13 Can science and technology alone solve emotional problems?

Another limitation is in the area of medical science. While scientific research has eliminated diseases like smallpox, it cannot do the same for other diseases. Cancer and AIDS patients have better chances of survival, but they still cannot be cured.

Researchers will go on to find a cure, but at the same time, new diseases like the (Avian) bird flu will continue to appear.

To fight problems like this, our whole society must come together as one to share information and resources.

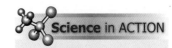

Exploring Further

When a person is out of a job, technology alone may not be able to help him get re-employed. He will need help from his family or even the community. In what areas can his family and community help?

Key Points

1. Technology is the application of scientific knowledge for the use and benefit of mankind.

2. Though the applications of science benefit our society, they also cause societal problems and raise moral and social issues.

3. Adopting the right attitudes in science helps to prevent the abuse and misuse of science and technology and to avoid societal problems such as pollution.

4. Science and technology are used to solve societal problems, but within their limits.

Let's Review!

1. What is technology?

2. Describe three examples of how the use of science and technology has:

    (a) benefited our society;   (b) harmed our society.

3. Science and technology cannot solve failed relationships between people. Describe another limitation of science and technology.

4. What are the advantages of working as a team to solve societal problems using technology?

▶**Revision 2 T.W.**

At a GLANCE

Study the following concept map for this chapter.

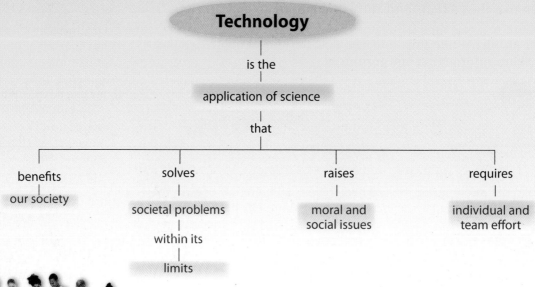

Technology

is the

application of science

that

| benefits | solves | raises | requires |

our society

societal problems

moral and social issues

individual and team effort

within its

limits

Think Tank

1. Do you agree with the statement 'Technology has improved our lives'? Give reasons to support your answer.

2. Study the following list of uses and benefits of science and technology to society.

> Science and technology have enabled us to:
> - lead an easier and more comfortable life;
> - fight and prevent diseases;
> - fulfil our water, food and energy needs;
> - produce better materials and innovative machines;
> - communicate in many more ways by using the Internet;
> - travel faster and easier to distant places;
> - explore outer space;
> - understand the causes and consequences of natural phenomena;
> - solve environmental problems like air, land and water pollution;
> - solve societal problems like traffic congestion.

Discuss with your classmates how the different uses of science and technology described in the above list have benefited our society.

▶**Portfolio Assessment 2 T.W.**

Measurement

Making Measurements
- Use of Measuring Instruments
- Physical Quantities & Units

• Overview •

Measuring helps us to be more objective when we interact with the environment. It happens every day – not just in the laboratories but also in our daily activities. It helps us to plan and improve the way we use our resources.

In this theme, we will look at how we can measure various physical quantities accurately, by using appropriate instruments and methods. We will also examine how we can describe different physical quantities better with appropriate units. By making direct measurements and using formulas, we will learn how to obtain physical quantities like density and speed.

• Key Inquiry Questions •

- Why is it important to have clearly defined quantities and units in measurement?
- How does the object or system you want to study determine the way in which you take the measurements?

3

Use of Measuring Instruments

In this chapter, you will learn to:

- show an understanding that different instruments are used to measure different physical quantities accurately

- make estimations and measurements of length, area, volume, mass, time and temperature, including:
  – area of irregular two-dimensional figures
  – volume and mass of liquids and solids (but not of gases)

- use common laboratory equipment such as the Bunsen burner, microscope, electronic balance and stopwatch in experimentation

- show an appreciation of scientific attitudes such as precision and accuracy in making measurements

What is the physical quantity being measured in the photograph?

Science is about understanding the world around us.

Scientists do this by making observations of physical quantities. A physical quantity is something that can be measured.

Measurement and estimation are not only important in scientific experiments; they are just as important in our daily activities.

Look carefully at the photographs below. Each photograph shows a daily activity which involves the measurement of a physical quantity.

Fig. 3.1 A research scientist measures the exact amount of chemicals to be put into a flask.

Fig. 3.2 A Chinese physician uses a beam balance to measure the amount of herbs.

Fig. 3.3 A timekeeper uses a stopwatch to measure how long a runner takes to finish a race.

In what ways are measurement and estimation important in the above activities?

Fig. 3.4 What are the advantages of estimating the size or magnitude of a physical quantity before it is measured?

The land area of Singapore is small with an area of about 648.1 km². Is area a physical quantity? Give a reason. Why is it important for the land area of Singapore to be increased?

3.1 Measuring Length

Length is the distance between two points. There are many different units for length, but the system of units we use is known as the SI unit. The SI unit for length is the **metre** (symbol: **m**).

Look at your ruler – does it measure length in metres or centimetres (symbol: cm)? How are the units related? What other units can your ruler measure length in?

Lengths range from the very small to the extremely large, as shown in Fig. 3.5 below. Draw a dot on the scale given in the diagram to show the position of your height.

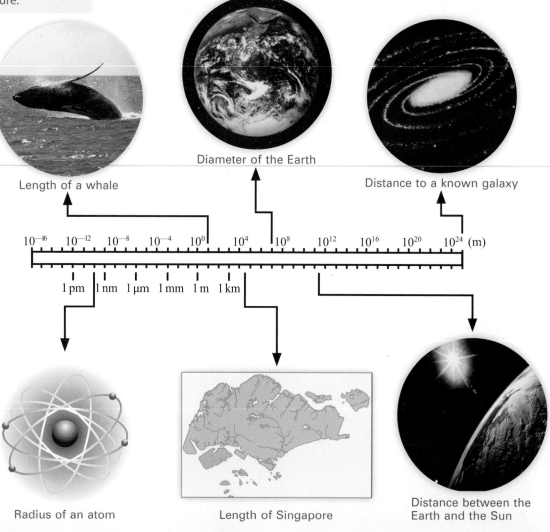

Fig. 3.5 Lengths range from the very small to the extremely large.

Metre Rule

The metre rule is commonly used to measure length in millimetres and centimetres with an accuracy of 1 mm or 0.1 cm. What is the shortest length that can be measured using the metre rule?

Fig. 3.6 A metre rule

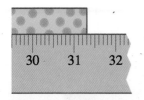

Try This!

1. Observe the divisions on the scale of a metre rule.

2. Count and record the number of divisions on the scale.

3. What is the length of each division on the scale?

4. Record your findings in your science portfolio.

To measure length using a metre rule,

length = 1.8 cm

The zero marking on the metre rule is first lined up with one end of the object to be measured.

The scale division on the metre rule that is closest to the other end of the object gives its length.

Fig. 3.7 How to measure length using a metre rule

Look at the following readings shown in the diagrams below. Assuming the zero marking on the metre rule is lined up with one end of the object being measured, what is the length of each object shown by its reading on the metre rule?

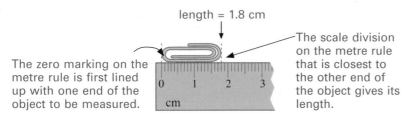

length =_____cm   length =_____cm   length =_____cm   length =_____cm

Fig. 3.8 What is the length of each object being measured by the metre rule?

▶Activity 5 P.B.

Parallax Error

Attach a measuring tape on the wall, with one end just touching the floor. Get your tallest classmate to stand against it. Can you read his or her height accurately off the measuring tape?

Fig. 3.9 How can we get an accurate reading of each other's height?

You will not able to measure your classmate's height accurately because of **parallax error**. This kind of error is partly because your eye is at an incorrect position and partly because the top of his or her head is not touching the scale of the measuring tape!

What must you do to make sure your eye is at the right position? What can your taller classmate do to avoid parallax error and make sure he or she can get an accurate measurement of your height?

Parallax error can occur when taking readings from rulers. The diagram below shows how parallax error can occur when taking a reading off a ruler:

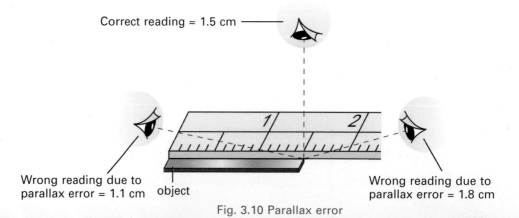

Correct reading = 1.5 cm

Wrong reading due to parallax error = 1.1 cm   object

Wrong reading due to parallax error = 1.8 cm

Fig. 3.10 Parallax error

Note that the eye must be placed directly above the marking of the ruler.

You can avoid parallax error when using the metre rule by

- positioning the eye vertically above the marking on the scale to be read;
- placing the metre rule on its edge beside the object to be measured so that the scale is touching the object;
- using a thin rule so that the scale is touching the object to be measured.

Fig. 3.11 Correct readings of 20.0 cm are obtained.

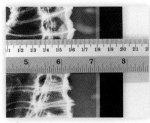

Exploring Further

The end of a half-metre rule with the zero mark worn out is shown in the diagram below. How would you use the half-metre rule without the zero mark to measure length?

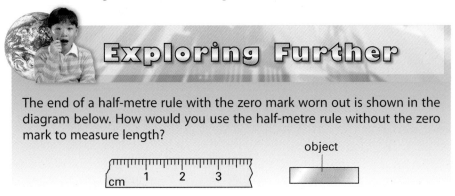

Vernier Calipers

Try using a ruler to find the diameter of a glass marble. You will find that the ruler is not a suitable instrument to use in this case. What difficulties will you run into?

Unlike a ruler, a pair of vernier calipers can be used to measure the diameter of a glass marble. It can measure short lengths with an accuracy of 0.01 cm or 0.1 mm.

Observe the labelled parts of the vernier calipers shown in the diagram below. What do the jaws and tail of the vernier calipers measure?

Fig. 3.12 A glass marble

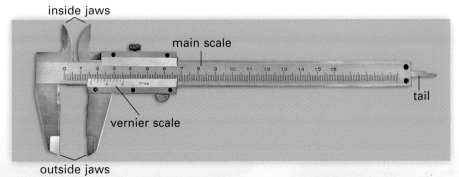

Fig. 3.13 A pair vernier calipers

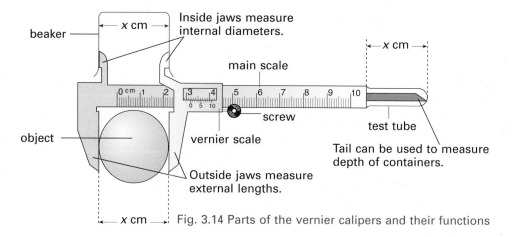

Fig. 3.14 Parts of the vernier calipers and their functions

To read the vernier calipers, follow two simple steps:

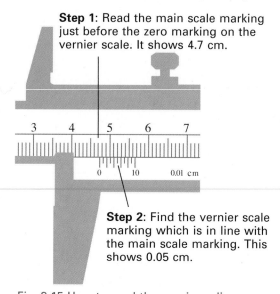

Step 1: Read the main scale marking just before the zero marking on the vernier scale. It shows 4.7 cm.

Step 2: Find the vernier scale marking which is in line with the main scale marking. This shows 0.05 cm.

Fig. 3.15 How to read the vernier calipers

Thus, the reading on the vernier calipers is 4.75 cm.

Zero Error

Zero error is a non-zero reading shown on a scale when the jaws of the vernier calipers are fully closed and nothing is being measured.

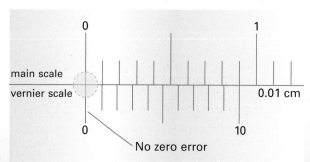

Fig. 3.16 No zero error

Close the jaws of a pair of vernier calipers fully. Do the zero marks on the main scale and the vernier scale coincide to form a straight line such as in Fig. 3.16? If they do not, we say that the vernier calipers have a zero error.

▶ **Activity 6 P.B.**

For measuring instruments with zero error, their readings should be corrected using the following formula:

> Corrected reading = Reading on the instrument – Zero error

Positive zero error

If the zero mark on the vernier scale is to the right of the zero mark on the main scale, there is a positive zero error. The zero error in Fig. 3.17 is +0.02 cm (read the vernier scale from the *left*).

If the vernier calipers shown in Fig. 3.17 is used to measure the length of an object and shows a reading of 5.24 cm, then the
actual (corrected) reading = 5.24 cm – (+0.02 cm)
= 5.22 cm

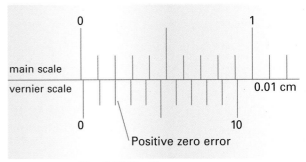

Fig. 3.17 Positive zero error

Negative zero error

If the zero mark on the vernier scale is to the left of the zero mark on the main scale, there is a negative zero error. The zero error in Fig. 3.18 is –0.04 cm (read the vernier scale from the *right*).

If the vernier calipers shown in Fig. 3.18 is used to measure the length of an object and shows a reading of 5.24 cm, then the
actual (corrected) reading = 5.24 cm – (–0.04 cm)
= 5.24 cm + 0.04 cm
= 5.28 cm

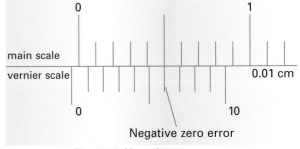

Fig. 3.18 Negative zero error

3.2 Measuring Area

Fig. 3.19 Sentosa Island covers an area of about 3.35 km².

Fig. 3.20 The area of a wall tile is about 400 cm².

Where am I?

Map of Southeast Asia

Why is Singapore often represented by a dot on the map?

Area is a measure of the size or extent of a surface. We use the SI unit, **square metre (m²)** to describe area.

The area of a large piece of land like a plantation is often described in hectares. How many square metres are there in one hectare?

How to Find the Area of:
• *regular two-dimensional plane surfaces*

The areas of some regular two-dimensional plane surfaces can be calculated using the formulae shown in Fig. 3.21.

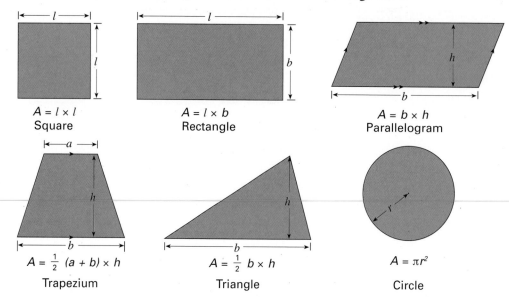

$A = l \times l$
Square

$A = l \times b$
Rectangle

$A = b \times h$
Parallelogram

$A = \frac{1}{2}\,(a + b) \times h$
Trapezium

$A = \frac{1}{2}\,b \times h$
Triangle

$A = \pi r^2$
Circle

Fig. 3.21 Area (*A*) of regular surfaces

• *irregular two-dimensional plane surfaces*

The area of an irregular two-dimensional plane surface can be estimated using small unit squares of known areas and counting them.

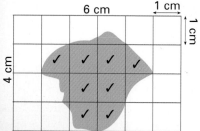

Fig. 3.22 Measuring area of irregular plane surface using unit squares

1. Place an irregular plane surface on a piece of graph paper with unit squares (Fig. 3.22).
2. Draw the outline of the irregular plane surface on the graph paper.
3. An incomplete unit square lying inside the outline is counted only if half or more than half of the incomplete unit square lies inside the outline.

Example

Total number of squares ≈ 8
Area of one square = 1 cm x 1 cm = 1 cm²
Area of the irregular plane surface ≈ 8 x 1 cm² ≈ 8 cm²

▶Activity 8 P.B.

Would the estimations of the areas of irregular two-dimensional plane surfaces be more accurate if unit squares of smaller known areas are used (Fig. 3.23)?

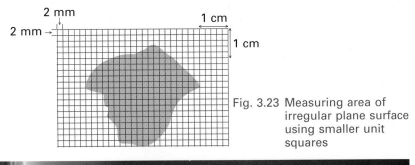

Fig. 3.23 Measuring area of irregular plane surface using smaller unit squares

3.3 Measuring Volume

Volume is a measure of the space occupied by an object. The SI unit for volume is the **cubic metre (m^3)**. Why is it important for the volumes of the following items to be measured accurately?

Fig. 3.24 A dose of medicine

Fig. 3.25 Petrol

How to Find the Volume of Liquids:

Instruments commonly used for measuring the volumes of liquids are the measuring cylinder, burette and pipette.

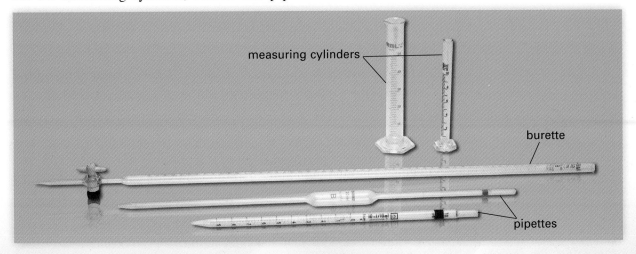

measuring cylinders

burette

pipettes

Fig. 3.26 Common laboratory instruments for measuring volume of liquids

Measuring Cylinder

The measuring cylinder is commonly used to measure the volume of liquids.

How to measure the volume of a liquid using a measuring cylinder:
1. Place a measuring cylinder on a flat horizontal surface.
2. Pour the liquid into the measuring cylinder.
3. Observe the bottom of the curved surface or **meniscus** of the liquid in the measuring cylinder.

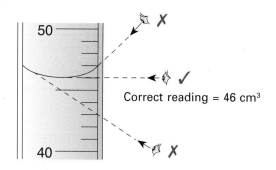

Correct reading = 46 cm³

Correct reading = 47 cm³

Fig. 3.27 Meniscus in most liquids such as water curve as shown.

Fig. 3.28 Meniscus in some liquids such as mercury curve as shown.

For most liquids, the meniscus curves as shown in Fig. 3.27. Position your eye at the same level as the bottom of the meniscus. The mark that corresponds to the bottom of the meniscus is taken as the reading.

For mercury, the meniscus curves as shown in Fig. 3.28. Position your eye at the same level as the top of the meniscus. The mark that corresponds to the top of the meniscus is taken as the reading.

We can avoid parallax error by placing the eye at the same level as the meniscus.

How to Find the Volume of:
• *regular-shaped solid objects*

The volume of regular-shaped objects can be calculated using the formulae shown in the diagrams below.

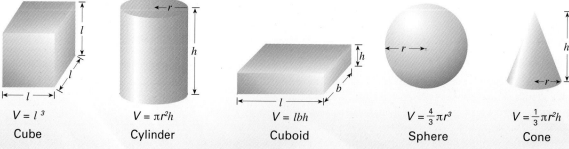

Cube	Cylinder	Cuboid	Sphere	Cone
$V = l^3$	$V = \pi r^2 h$	$V = lbh$	$V = \frac{4}{3}\pi r^3$	$V = \frac{1}{3}\pi r^2 h$

Fig. 3.29 Volume(V) of some common regular-shaped objects

• small irregular-shaped solid objects

The volume of small irregular-shaped objects like a stone cannot be found by formula. Since it sinks in water, we can use the displacement of water to find its volume:

Using only a measuring cylinder:

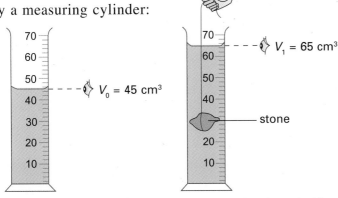

Fig. 3.30 Measuring the volume of a small irregular-shaped object

Volume of irregular-shaped object,
$V = V_1 - V_0 = 65 - 45 = 20$ cm^3

• large irregular-shaped solid objects

Using a measuring cylinder and a displacement can:

Step 1
- Fill the can with water until excess water flows out of its spout into a beaker.
- Remove the beaker when water stops flowing into it (Fig. 3.31(a)).

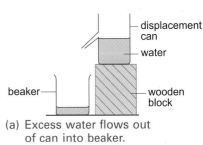

(a) Excess water flows out of can into beaker.

Step 2
- Place an empty measuring cylinder below the spout of the displacement can.
- Tie the irregular-shaped object with a piece of string.
- Lower it gently into the displacement can until it is fully immersed in the water (Fig. 3.31(b)).

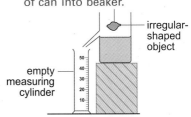

(b) The object is lowered into the displacement can.

Step 3
- When the water stops flowing into the measuring cylinder, observe and record the volume of water displaced by the object and collected in the measuring cylinder (Fig. 3.31(c)).

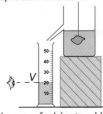

(c) Volume of object = V

For both methods, you must lower the stone gently into water so that the water will not splash out. Why?

Fig. 3.31 Steps for measuring the volume of a large irregular-shaped object

▶Activity 9 P.B.

Exploring Further

Can you use the two methods shown in Fig. 3.30 and Fig. 3.31 on page 35 to find the volume of a

- piece of candy;
- styrofoam block;
- glass pebble?

If not, give reasons and suggest how you can change these methods to find the volume. Record your reasoning and suggestions in your science portfolio.

3.4 Measuring Mass

Mass is a measure of the quantity or amount of matter in an object. The SI unit for mass is the **kilogram (kg)**.

The following pictures show that there are other units of mass:

Fig. 3.32 A grain of rice has a mass of about 0.02 mg.

Fig. 3.33 Sugar is normally sold in packets, each of mass 1 kg.

Fig. 3.34 A 40 tonne lorry

Instruments for Measuring Mass

Lever balance

Electronic balance

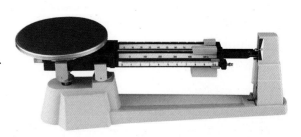

Triple beam balance

Fig. 3.35 Some instruments for measuring mass

Which type of balance is most commonly used in the school laboratory and why? What is the smallest reading this balance can give?

3.5 Measuring Time

How do you normally spend your time every day? The photographs below show two events that you may have experienced.

Fig. 3.36 A 100 m race   Fig. 3.37 Taking one's pulse

Time can refer to an instant or interval. The SI for time is the **second (s)**. It is sometimes not practical to use seconds to measure time. Why? What other units do we measure time in?

Instruments for Measuring Time

The photographs below show different kinds of instruments for measuring time. In the science laboratory, the stopwatch is commonly used to record time intervals.

Wrist watch   Alarm clock

Sundial   Hourglass   Pendulum clock

Fig. 3.38 Some instruments for measuring time

Mechanical stopwatch

The mechanical stopwatch consists of a minute scale and a second scale.

- The minute scale is the small circle at the top of the face of the stopwatch;
- The second scale is the big circle on the same face.

The mechanical stopwatch can measure time intervals accurate to 0.1 s or 0.2 s.

Fig. 3.39 shows you how to read the mechanical stopwatch.

[2] min [7.4] s

minute hand
second hand

Fig. 3.39 Mechanical stopwatch

Try This!

What are the readings shown by these stopwatches?

[ ] min [ ] s   [ ] min [ ] s

Electronic stopwatch

The electronic stopwatch is more accurate than the mechanical stopwatch. It has a digital display and can measure time intervals accurate to 0.01 s. It can measure time intervals in hours too.

Fig. 3.40 shows you how to read the electronic stopwatch.

[2] min [39 . 54 s]

Fig. 3.40 Electronic stopwatch

Exploring Further

An atomic clock is the most accurate and precise device for measuring time. At present, the NIST-F1 is the world's most accurate clock. It has an accuracy of one second in twenty million years. How does the atomic clock work?

For further information, log on to:
http://science.howstuffworks.com/atomic-clock1.htm

▶ Activity 7, 10 P.B.

3.6 Measuring Temperature

Temperature is important in the following activities:

Fig. 3.41 Baking bread

Fig. 3.42 Bathing a newborn baby

Temperature is a measure of how hot a substance is. The SI unit for temperature is the **kelvin (K)**. Other units include degree Celsius (°C) and degree Fahrenheit (°F).

You can convert temperature from degree Celsius to kelvin by using the following formula:

$$\text{Temperature (K)} - 273 = \text{Temperature (°C)}$$

Instruments for Measuring Temperature

One way to measure temperature objectively is by using a thermometer. You have most probably seen a digital ear thermometer or a clinical thermometer when you visit the doctor.

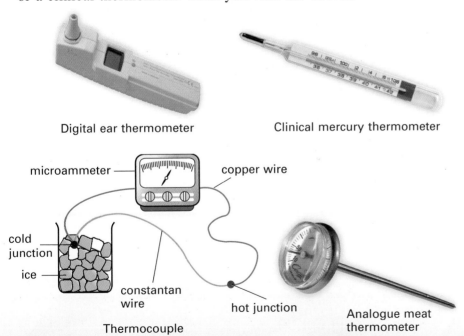

Digital ear thermometer

Clinical mercury thermometer

microammeter — copper wire

cold junction

ice

constantan wire

hot junction

Thermocouple

Analogue meat thermometer

Fig. 3.43 Some instruments for measuring temperature

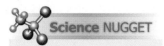
The laboratory thermometer

The laboratory thermometer is a liquid-in-glass thermometer. Your teacher will show you a laboratory thermometer like this:

Fig. 3.44 Laboratory thermometer

Handle the thermometer with care as it is mostly made of glass. Examine it carefully. The smallest division on the thermometer is usually 1 °C or 0.1 °C.

The lowest and highest temperatures you can read with this thermometer are -10 °C and 110 °C respectively. These two temperatures define the range of the thermometer.

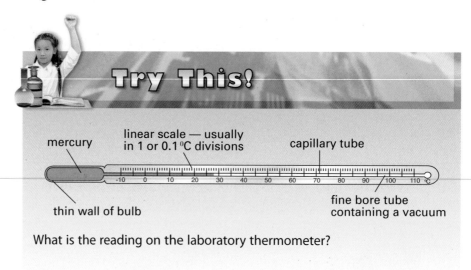

mercury

linear scale — usually in 1 or 0.1 °C divisions

capillary tube

thin wall of bulb

fine bore tube containing a vacuum

What is the reading on the laboratory thermometer?

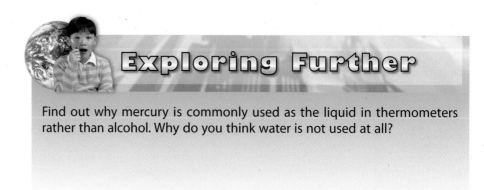

Exploring Further

Find out why mercury is commonly used as the liquid in thermometers rather than alcohol. Why do you think water is not used at all?

▶Activity 3 T.W.

Key Points

1. A physical quantity is a quantity which can be measured.

2. Length is the distance between two points. The SI unit for length is the metre (m).

3. The metre rule measures length in millimetres and centimetres with an accuracy of 1 mm or 0.1 cm.

4. Vernier calipers measure short lengths in millimetres and centimetres with an accuracy of 0.1 mm or 0.01 cm.

5. Parallax error is an error in a measurement due to the eye not being in the correct position when taking a reading.

6. Zero error is a non-zero reading shown on a scale when nothing is being measured.

7. Area is a measure of the size or extent of a surface. The SI unit for area is the square metre (m^2).

8. The area of a regular two-dimensional plane surface is determined by measuring the appropriate lengths and then calculating the area based on a formula.

9. The area of an irregular two-dimensional plane surface is estimated using small unit squares of known areas and counting them.

10. Volume is a measure of the space occupied by an object. The SI unit for volume is the cubic metre (m^3).

11. The volume of a regular-shaped object is determined by measuring the appropriate lengths and then calculating the volume based on a formula.

12. The volume of an irregular-shaped solid object can be found by the displacement method.

13. Mass is a measure of the quantity or amount of matter in an object. The SI unit for mass is the kilogram (kg).

14. The electronic balance and beam balance are commonly used to measure mass.

15. Time is an instant or an interval. The SI unit for time is the second (s).

16. Stopwatches are commonly used to measure time intervals.

17. Temperature is a measure of how hot a substance is. The SI unit for temperature is the kelvin (K).

18. Thermometers are commonly used to measure temperature.

1. Name an appropriate instrument to measure

    (a) the amount of liquid in a can of soda;

    (b) a person's waist;

    (c) the thickness of a $1 coin;

    (d) the distance an athlete covers in a long jump.

2.

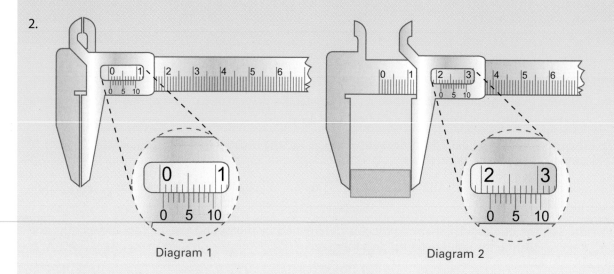

Diagram 1   Diagram 2

Diagram 1 shows the reading on the vernier calipers when its jaws are closed.

Diagram 2 shows the reading on the same vernier calipers when an object is gripped between its jaws.

(a) What is the zero error of the vernier calipers?

(b) What is the length of the object?

(c) State two advantages of using the vernier calipers instead of the metre rule to measure the length of the object.

3.

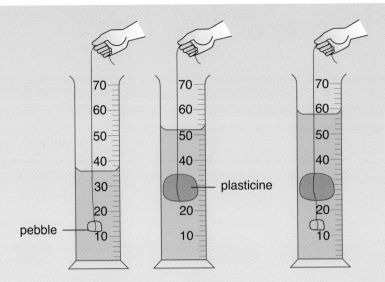

pebble

plasticine

The above measuring cylinders are filled with equal amounts of water.

(a) Write down the reading of the measuring cylinder that contains

    (i)   water and pebble;

    (ii) water and plasticine;

    (iii) water, pebble and plasticine.

(b) Find the volume of

    (i)   water used to fill each measuring cylinder;

    (ii) the pebble;

    (iii) the plasticine.

4. (a) What is the accuracy of the mechanical stopwatch shown on the right?

  (b) What is the time shown by the stopwatch?

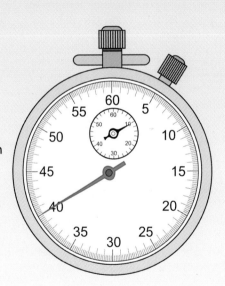

5.

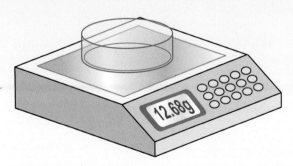

  (a) Name the instrument shown above.

  (b) What are the advantages of using this instrument?

Complete the following concept map for this chapter.

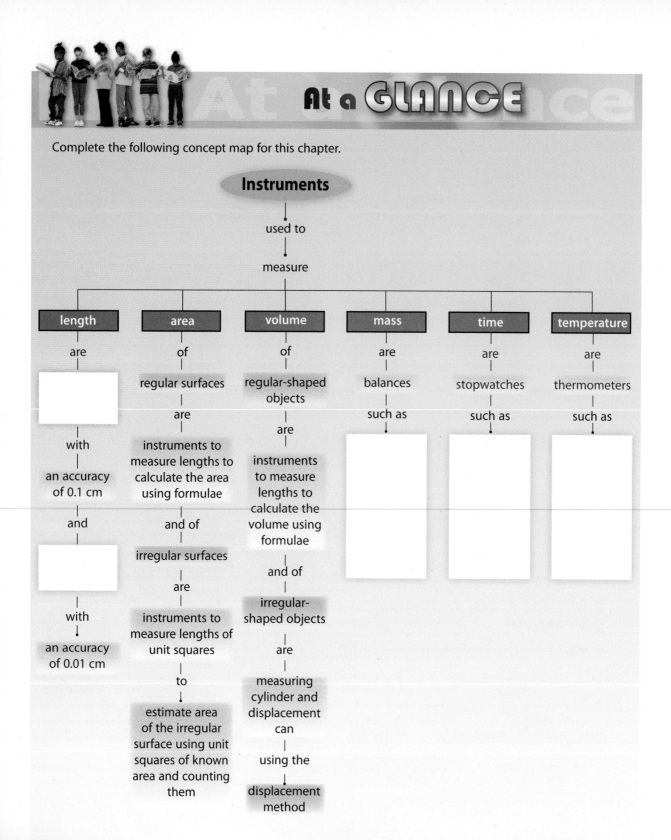

Instruments

used to

measure

| length | area | volume | mass | time | temperature |

length
are

[blank]

with

an accuracy of 0.1 cm

and

[blank]

with

an accuracy of 0.01 cm

area
of

regular surfaces

are

instruments to measure lengths to calculate the area using formulae

and of

irregular surfaces

are

instruments to measure lengths of unit squares

to

estimate area of the irregular surface using unit squares of known area and counting them

volume
of

regular-shaped objects

are

instruments to measure lengths to calculate the volume using formulae

and of

irregular-shaped objects

are

measuring cylinder and displacement can

using the

displacement method

mass
are

balances

such as

[blank]

time
are

stopwatches

such as

[blank]

temperature
are

thermometers

such as

[blank]

With a few of your classmates, come up with a classification table to classify the instruments covered in this chapter. Compare your table with those of your classmates. In what ways are your classification tables similar or different?

Think Tank

1. Why is it desirable for scientists to use the SI units in their work?

2. It is easy to measure the length of a pole or the diameter of a ball bearing but how can one measure vast distances such as the depth of a deep ocean or the diameter of the Earth?

3. Find out what a tangram is. Make one and use it to make the shapes shown by your teacher. Is the area of each shape the same? How can the area be found?

4. When the metric system was introduced in 1792, a 10-hour clock was proposed. However, the proposal was never accepted and eventually abandoned. Would you have accepted the use of a 10-hour clock? Why?

5. Why are sundials inaccurate for measuring time?

▶ Portfolio Assessment 3 T.W.

Physical Quantities and Units

In this chapter, you will learn to:

- identify and use the appropriate units for different physical quantities

- use the appropriate units for length, mass, time and temperature

- relate and use the appropriate prefixes, milli-, centi- or kilo- in relation to the units of length and mass

- explain what is meant by density

- calculate density using the formula: $\text{Density} = \dfrac{\text{Mass}}{\text{Volume}}$

- predict whether objects sink or float using the concept of density

- determine appropriate units for physical quantities such as area, volume, density and rate

- explain what is meant by average speed

- calculate average speed using the formula:

  $\text{Average speed} = \dfrac{\text{Distance travelled}}{\text{Time taken}}$

- solve problems of objects in motion using the concept of speed

- show an appreciation of scientific attitudes such as objectivity, integrity and open-mindedness in collecting and analysing data

How can such a large and heavy hot-air balloon rise up in the air?

Some physical quantities can be measured directly with an instrument...

Fig. 4.1 Mass of person

Fig. 4.2 Height of a person

...while others can be found by taking measurements of other physical quantities.

Fig. 4.3 Speed can be found by measuring length and time.

All these physical quantities can be further expressed by using appropriate units and prefixes.

In the coming sections, we will examine how to describe physical quantities using units and prefixes. We will also look into the physical quantities like speed and density, which are based on other physical quantities.

4.1 Physical Quantities, SI Units and Prefixes

Every measurement of a physical quantity consists of two parts, a number and a unit.

For example,

Length of a running track	=	400	m
↓		↓	↓
physical quantity		number	unit

In Singapore, most people use SI units like the metre or centimetre to describe length. However, in Britain, a different system of units (Imperial units) like inch and foot are more commonly used for describing lengths. Confusion over units may occur if the different systems of units are used to describe the same quantity.

Fig. 4.4 Using different units to describe the same quantity can cause confusion.

Connect

Have you noticed the unit for volume of petrol sold at petrol kiosks in Singapore? Find out if similar units are used in countries like Britain and the United States.

To reduce confusion, many countries have agreed to adopt the **metric system**. This system is easy to use because its units of different sizes are related by powers of ten (decimals).

Since 1960, scientists worldwide have agreed to use a single system of units for science and research – the **International System of Units** or **SI units**, which is adapted from the metric system. This system allows scientists to share and understand information more easily.

The SI units consist of seven base quantities. In this course, you will only look at five of them. They are shown in Table 4.1.

Science NUGGET

The units for all physical quantities other than the base quantities are derived from the base units. For example, the derived unit of area, the square metre, is derived from the metre.

Base quantity	Base unit	Symbol
Length	metre	m
Mass	kilogram	kg
Time	second	s
Temperature	kelvin	K
Electric current	ampere	A

Table 4.1 Base quantities and units

Larger and smaller units for the same measured physical quantity have names that are clearly related to the fundamental unit. The names of the larger or smaller units normally begin with a prefix. Some common prefixes and their meanings are shown in Table 4.2.

Prefix	Symbol	Meaning			Example
tera	T	One trillion	(1 000 000 000 000	or 10^{12})	terametre
giga	G	One billion	(1 000 000 000	or 10^{9})	gigabyte
mega	M	One million	(1 000 000	or 10^{6})	megawatt
kilo	k	One thousand	(1 000	or 10^{3})	kilovolt
hecto	h	One hundred	(100	or 10^{2})	hectometre
deca	da	One ten	(10	or 10)	decagram
deci	d	One tenth	(1/10	or 10^{-1})	decimetre
centi	c	One hundredth	(1/100	or 10^{-2})	centimetre
milli	m	One thousandth	(1/1 000	or 10^{-3})	milliampere
micro	μ	One millionth	(1/1 000 000	or 10^{-6})	microgram
nano	n	One billionth	(1/1 000 000 000	or 10^{-9})	nanosecond
pico	p	One trillionth	(1/1 000 000 000 000	or 10^{-12})	picofarad

Table 4.2 Some prefixes. Can the above prefixes be applied to all SI units?

Try This!

1. Convert each of the following lengths to metres:
   (a) 1.8 mm   (b) 0.7 cm   (c) 3.4 km

2. Convert 0.038 kg to its equivalent in:
   (a) mg   (b) cg   (c) g

Connect

When did Singapore officially switch from the Imperial system of units to the metric system? Why? (Hint: More than 30 years ago!)

▶Activity 4.1 T.W.

4.2 Density

Which is heavier – an iron nail or a wooden stool?

Fig. 4.5 Iron nail

Fig. 4.6 Wooden stool

However, if you compare 1 cm³ of iron with 1 cm³ of wood, which is heavier?

The iron has more mass packed into one cubic centimetre compared to the wood. We say that the density of iron is higher than the density of wood.

The **density** of a substance is its **mass per unit volume**. It is found by dividing the mass of a substance by its volume and can be written as an equation:

$$\text{Density} = \frac{\text{Mass}}{\text{Volume}} \quad \text{or} \quad D = \frac{m}{V} \quad \text{or} \quad \rho = \frac{m}{V}$$

where D or ρ is density, m is mass, and V is volume.

If mass is measured in kg and the volume in m³, what is the SI unit for density?

Another common unit for density is g/cm³. Convert 1 g/cm³ to its equivalent in kg/m³:

$$1 \text{ g/cm}^3 = \underline{\hspace{3cm}} \text{ kg/m}^3$$

The pictures below show a cube of copper and a cube of styrofoam. Can you calculate their respective densities?

Fig. 4.7 1 cm³ of copper has a mass of 8.9 g. The density of copper is _____ g/cm³.

Fig. 4.8 1 m³ of styrofoam has a mass of 80 kg. The density of styrofoam is _____ kg/m³.

The Density Equation

The density equation can be written in three different ways:

Density = $\dfrac{\text{Mass}}{\text{Volume}}$	Volume = $\dfrac{\text{Mass}}{\text{Density}}$	Mass = Density × Volume
Example: Find the density of 300 cm³ of lead which has a mass of 3 420 g. Mass = 3 420 g Volume = 300 cm³ Density = $\dfrac{\text{Mass}}{\text{Volume}}$ $= \dfrac{3\ 420}{300}$ g/cm³ $= 11.4$ g/cm³	*Example:* 28 kg of petrol has a density of 700 kg/m³. Find its volume in cm³. Mass = 28 kg Density = 700 kg/m³ Volume = $\dfrac{\text{Mass}}{\text{Density}}$ $= \dfrac{28}{700}$ m³ $= 0.04$ m³ $= 0.04 \times 1\ 000\ 000$ cm³ $= 40\ 000$ cm³	*Example:* The density of copper is 8 900 kg/m³. If the volume of a piece of copper is 500 cm³, find its mass. Density = 8 900 kg/m³ Volume = 500 cm³ $= \dfrac{500}{1\ 000\ 000}$ m³ $= \dfrac{5}{10\ 000}$ m³ Mass = Density × Volume $= 8\ 900 \times \dfrac{5}{10\ 000}$ kg $= 4.45$ kg

Table 4.3 Three different ways to write the density equation

Here is an easy-to-remember aid for using the formula $D = \dfrac{m}{V}$.

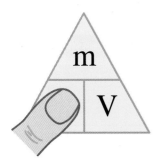

Fig. 4.9 To find *D*, cover *D* in the triangle. What remains is $\frac{m}{V}$ which equals *D*.

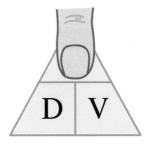

Fig. 4.10 To find *m*, cover *m* in the triangle. What remains is *D* × *V* which equals *m*.

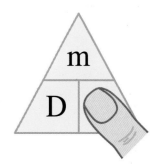

Fig. 4.11 To find *V*, cover *V* in the triangle. What remains is $\frac{m}{D}$ which equals *V*.

Finding the Density of a Substance

You can find the density of a substance in three steps:

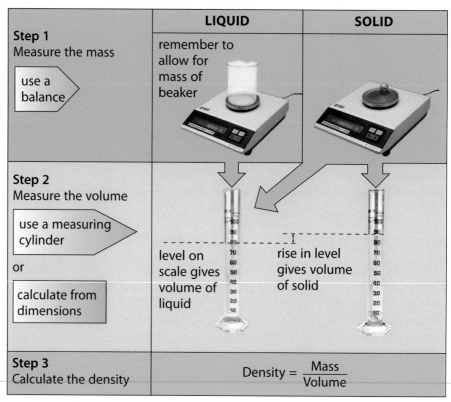

	LIQUID	**SOLID**
Step 1 Measure the mass use a balance	remember to allow for mass of beaker	
Step 2 Measure the volume use a measuring cylinder or calculate from dimensions	level on scale gives volume of liquid	rise in level gives volume of solid
Step 3 Calculate the density	Density = $\dfrac{\text{Mass}}{\text{Volume}}$	

Table 4.4 Finding the density of a liquid and solid

Table 4.5 shows the densities of some common materials.

State	Materials	Density (g/cm³)
Solid	Platinum	21.5
	Gold	19.3
	Lead	11.3
	Silver	10.5
	Copper	8.9
	Iron	7.9
	Zinc	7.1
	Aluminium	2.7
	Glass	2.5
	Ice	0.92
	Pinewood	0.50
	Cork	0.24

State	Materials	Density (g/cm³)
Liquid	Mercury	13.6
	Glycerine	1.3
	Seawater	1.03
	Pure water (at 4 °C)	1.00
	Olive oil	0.92
	Turpentine	0.87
	Petrol	0.80
	Alcohol	0.79
Gas	Air	0.001 29
	Hydrogen	0.000 09

Table 4.5 Densities of some materials

Answer the following questions with reference to Table 4.5.
(a) Which state of matter has the lowest density?
(b) Which liquid has the highest density?
(c) Which one of the following states normally has the highest density – solid, liquid or gas?
(d) Which solid with a mass of 1 kg has the smallest volume?
(e) Which liquid with a volume of 1 cm³ has the largest mass?

Density is a useful property for identifying materials.

Doctors, food inspectors and engineers are just a few of the people who rely on density and other properties every day to help identify substances.

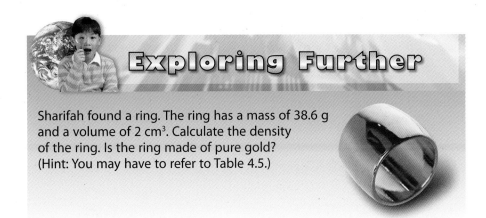

Exploring Further

Sharifah found a ring. The ring has a mass of 38.6 g and a volume of 2 cm³. Calculate the density of the ring. Is the ring made of pure gold? (Hint: You may have to refer to Table 4.5.)

Floating and Sinking

Have you ever wondered why some substances float, while others sink?

Fluids are substances which can flow. Examples of fluids are liquids and gases. Study the diagram below.

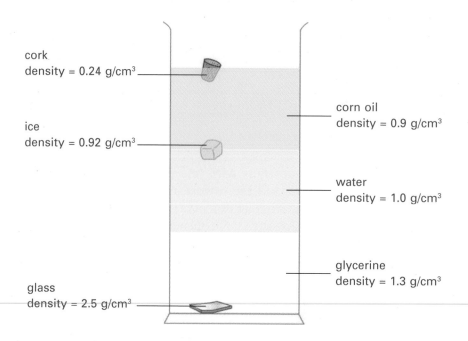

cork
density = 0.24 g/cm³

ice
density = 0.92 g/cm³

glass
density = 2.5 g/cm³

corn oil
density = 0.9 g/cm³

water
density = 1.0 g/cm³

glycerine
density = 1.3 g/cm³

Fig. 4.12 Substances of lower densities float in fluids of higher densities.

Compare the densities of the different materials.

In general, substances with lower densities float in fluids of higher densities.

What happens to a solid placed in a liquid if the densities of the solid and liquid are the same?

►Activity 4.2 T.W.

Try This!

1. Place an egg carefully into a beaker half-filled with water. The egg will sink.

2. Add salt to the water, one tablespoonful at a time. The egg will gradually float as more salt is added.

3. When the egg is floating at the surface of the salt water, carefully add more water by dribbling it slowly over a spoon held against the side of the glass. The egg will float on the boundary between the layer of fresh water and salt water.

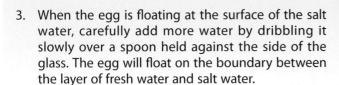

▶ Activity 11 P.B.

Science in ACTION

Airline pilots need to know the density of the air before taking off and landing as it affects the length of runway needed.

Engineers use the densities of materials to calculate the mass of their buildings and decide if the ground can support the mass of the buildings.

4.3 Rate

Turn on the fan and feel the air blowing on your face. If you adjust the fan to a higher setting, you will feel more air blowing at you every minute. We describe the amount of air per unit time as the rate of airflow.

Rate is a ratio between two physical quantities such as volume and time. It describes how a quantity changes with respect to time. The unit for the rate of a physical quantity is given by the ratio of the unit of the physical quantity to the unit of time.

Example

1. Speed $= \dfrac{\text{Distance travelled}}{\text{Time taken}}$

   SI unit for speed $= \dfrac{\text{SI unit for distance}}{\text{SI unit for time}}$

   $= \dfrac{\text{metre (m)}}{\text{second (s)}}$

   $= \text{metre/second (m/s)}$

2. Petrol consumption $= \dfrac{\text{Volume of petrol used}}{\text{Time taken}}$

   SI unit for petrol consumption $= \dfrac{\text{SI unit for volume}}{\text{SI unit for time}}$

   $= \dfrac{\text{cubic metre (m}^3\text{)}}{\text{second (s)}}$

   $= \text{cubic metre/second (m}^3\text{/s)}$

For practical reasons, not all rates describe how a quantity changes with time. Can you pick out one such rate among the following examples? What are the two physical quantities involved?

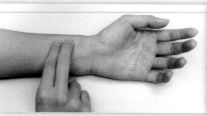

Fig. 4.13 Pulse rate is an important indicator of health. It is described in beats per minute. What is the pulse of a healthy person?

Fig. 4.14 Different vehicles have different rates of petrol consumption. It is usually described in litres per kilometre. Why do you think petrol consumption is higher when driving in the city than on the highway?

Fig. 4.15 The rate of increase in height is different at different stages of life. At which stages are the rates of increase highest?

Fig. 4.16 The rate of water flowing out from a fireman's hose must be fast enough to put out the fire effectively. Rate of water flow is described in litres per minute. Can the rate of water flowing from the fireman's hose be controlled?

How do the rates mentioned in the activities above affect you, your family and society?

4.4 Speed and Average Speed

Suppose you are running a 400 m race. You would want to record the time you take to complete the race, to know how fast you are compared to the other runners. Why is it important to you as a runner to know your speed?

Similarly, simply describing motion as 'fast' or 'slow' in science and telecommunications is not enough. Accurate measurements of distance and time are required.

Speed is the distance travelled per unit time or the rate of change of distance with respect to time. It is found by taking the distance travelled and dividing it by the time taken:

$$\text{Speed} = \frac{\text{Distance travelled}}{\text{Time taken}} \text{ or } v = \frac{d}{t}$$

where v is speed, d is distance travelled, and t is time taken.

The SI unit for speed is **metre per second (m/s)**. Other common units for speed are km/h and cm/s.

Example

Light takes 0.000 1 s to travel 30 000 m in vacuum. Find the speed of light in vacuum.

$$\text{Speed of light in vacuum} = \frac{\text{Distance travelled}}{\text{Time taken}}$$

$$= \frac{30\ 000 \text{ m}}{0.000\ 1 \text{ s}}$$

$$= 300\ 000\ 000 \text{ m/s}$$

$$= 3 \times 10^8 \text{ m/s}$$

Try This!

The distance between the Earth and the Sun is 149 000 000 km. The speed of light is 300 000 km/s. If the Sun stops giving out light now, how much longer will we be able to see the Sun?

▶Activity 12A–12B P.B.

Although some objects move at constant speeds, such as light in vacuum, most objects move at varying speeds.

The MRT train is one such example. You can 'feel' the change in speed of the train when you are travelling in it. Can you see the effect of this change in speed? When the MRT train travels from one station to another, when does it speed up or slow down?

A more suitable description of the motion of an object moving at varying speeds is its average speed. The **average speed** is found by dividing the total distance travelled by the total time taken to travel the distance and can be written as a formula:

$$\text{Average speed} = \frac{\text{Total distance travelled}}{\text{Total time taken}}$$

Example

A train took 11.5 minutes to travel 10 km from station X to station Y. It stopped at station Y for 0.5 minutes. It then took another 24.0 minutes to travel 20 km from station Y to station Z. What was the average speed of the train?

Time taken from X to Y = 11.5 min
Time at rest at Y   = 0.5 min
Time taken from Y to Z = 24.0 min

Distance from X to Y = 10 km
Distance from Y to Z = 20 km

Total distance travelled = 10 + 20 = 30 km
Total time taken = 11.5 + 0.5 + 24.0 = 36.0 min

$$\text{Average speed} = \frac{30 \text{ km}}{36 \text{ min}}$$
$$= \frac{30 \text{ km}}{(36/60) \text{ h}}$$
$$= 50 \text{ km/h}$$

Key Points

1. A physical quantity consists of a number and a unit.

2.

Base quantity	Base unit	Symbol
Length	metre	m
Mass	kilogram	kg
Time	second	s
Temperature	kelvin	K
Electric current	ampere	A

3. Prefixes like milli- or centi- are used in smaller units like millimetre and centimetre for length or milligram and centigram for mass.

4. The prefix kilo- is used in larger units like kilometre for length or kilogram for mass.

5. Rate describes how a physical quantity changes with respect to time.

6. Density is the mass per unit volume of a substance. Some appropriate units for density are kg/m^3 and g/cm^3.

7. The density equation is: $\text{Density} = \dfrac{\text{Mass}}{\text{Volume}}$

8. If a substance floats in a fluid, the density of the substance is less than the density of the fluid.

9. Rate is a ratio which describes how a physical quantity changes with respect to time.

10. Speed is the distance travelled per unit time. Some appropriate units for speed are m/s and km/h.

11. Average speed is equal to the total distance travelled divided by the total time taken to travel that distance. Some appropriate units for average speed are m/s and km/h.

1. Name two appropriate units commonly used in the measurement of your height. Which of the two units is more appropriate for the measurement of height? Why?

2. An adult passenger boarding an aircraft is only allowed to carry one piece of hand luggage into the aircraft cabin. Name an appropriate unit for the mass of the hand luggage.

3. A brick has a mass of 0.4 kilograms and a volume of 500 cubic centimetres. Find the density of the brick in units of:
   (a) g/cm^3
   (b) kg/m^3

4. Jack found a gold-coloured ring. Describe how you would help Jack to determine whether the ring is made of pure gold.

5. A cube of glass of volume 20 cm³ and mass 50 g is placed in 200 cm³ of glycerine of mass 260 g. Does the cube of glass float or sink in the glycerine? Why?

6. We often state that the speed of light in vacuum is about 3×10^8 m/s and the average speed of sound in air is about 330 m/s. Why do you think the term 'average' is used to describe the speed of sound in air but not the speed of light in vacuum?

7. An object moves at 5 km/h for 20 minutes and then moves at 10 km/h for 30 minutes. Find:
   (a) the total distance moved by the object;
   (b) the average speed of the object.

▶Revision 4 T.W.

Study the following concept map for this chapter.

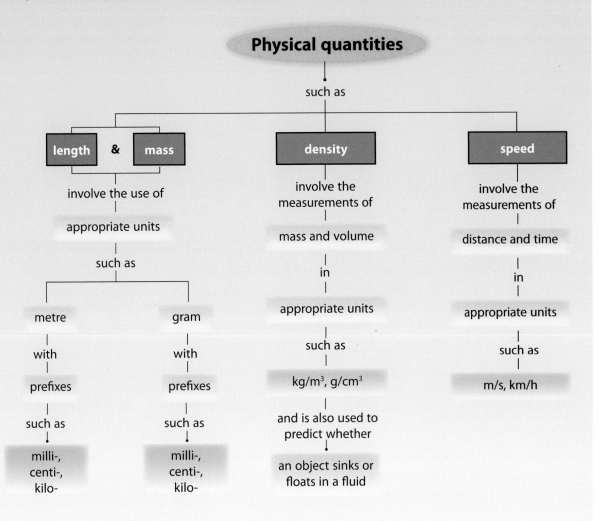

Physical quantities

such as

| length | & | mass | density | speed |

length & mass involve the use of appropriate units such as

metre — with — prefixes — such as → milli-, centi-, kilo-

gram — with — prefixes — such as → milli-, centi-, kilo-

density involve the measurements of mass and volume in appropriate units such as

kg/m^3, g/cm^3

and is also used to predict whether an object sinks or floats in a fluid

speed involve the measurements of distance and time in appropriate units such as

m/s, km/h

Create another concept map to classify the different units of physical quantities that you have learnt so far.

1. The formulae of some physical quantities are given below. From their formulae, deduce which quantities are rates and define them.

    (a) $\text{Power} = \dfrac{\text{Work done}}{\text{Time}}$

    (b) Mass = Density × Volume

    (c) $\text{Acceleration} = \dfrac{\text{Final speed} - \text{Initial speed}}{\text{Time}}$

    (d) Volume of cylinder = π × (radius)^2 × height

2. The nearest star to us, apart from the Sun, is 4.3 light years away from us. One light year is the distance travelled by light in 1 year.

    (a) How long does it take the light from this star to reach us?

    (b) Calculate the distance this star is away from us in km, given that the speed of light is 300 000 km/s.

    (c) Why is the light year used instead of the kilometre to measure the distances between the stars and us?

Diversity

Diversity of Matter
- Classification of Matter
- Elements, Compounds and Mixtures
- Solutions and Suspensions

Diversity of Plant and Animal Life
- Classification of Plant and Animal Life

• Overview •

The world is made up of a great variety of things – living and non-living – each with its own unique qualities.

In general, people, not just scientists, like to classify things around them according to their common properties or features. They organise the vast amount of information so as to understand the world better.

In this theme, we will examine the classification of living and non-living things, according to some common characteristics.

• Key Inquiry Questions •

- How does the diversity of living and non-living things around us affect our lives?
- How do we classify things in our world?

CHAPTER 5

Classification of Matter

In this chapter, you will learn to:

- classify a number of common everyday objects and recognise that there are many ways of classifying the same groups of objects

- describe the properties of groups of materials in terms of density, strength, hardness, flexibility, electrical conductivity, thermal conductivity, melting point and boiling point

- distinguish between the main classes of materials such as metals, glass, ceramics, plastics and fibres in terms of their properties

- use data on the properties of different materials to make evaluative judgements about their uses

- communicate your findings on classification and justify your reasons

- show an appreciation of Man's responsibility to have care and concern for the environment

- value individual effort and working in a team as part of scientific inquiry

What different materials are used to make a bicycle?
What property of each material is made use of here?

Putting information into groups is a human way of organising information. The photographs on the right show a few places where people classify things.

What are the different ways to classify things around us?

Fig. 5.1 Supermarket

Fig. 5.2 Bakery

5.1 Different Ways of Classifying Matter

How are the books in your school library classified?

Library books are usually classified into two main sets, such as fiction and non-fiction. A set is a group of objects with similar properties.

How are fiction books further classified? How does this classification help the librarian or yourself as a library user? Suggest another way to classify your school's library books.

Classification is the grouping of objects into sets according to one or more common properties. As an object can have many properties, there can also be more than one way to classify a group of objects.

Fig. 5.3 Library

Try This!

1. Gather all the stationery that you have in your schoolbag.

2. With a few of your classmates, classify the stationery according to shape.

3. Repeat Step 2 as many times as you can, using different classifications. How many different classifications did you make?

Scientists have classified matter in different ways to make the study of matter easier to understand.

Matter that is used for making objects is termed as a material. Classifying materials into different groups has made it easier for us to choose the right materials to make certain products. Which group of materials is most commonly used to make coins?

Fig. 5.4 Coins

▶ Activity 5.1 T.W.   ▶ Activity 13 P.B.

5.2 Physical Properties of Materials

Materials that have been chosen to make objects are often based on their physical properties. For example, diamond is used as a cutting tool because of its hardness.

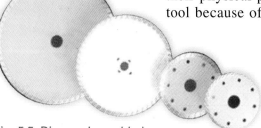

Fig. 5.5 Diamond saw blades cut everything, from asphalt to brick and concrete stone.

A physical property is any aspect of an object or substance that can be measured without changing its identity. Physical properties of matter include density, strength, hardness, flexibility, electrical conductivity, thermal conductivity, melting point and boiling point.

Density

The **density** of a substance is its mass per unit volume.

As different materials usually have different densities, the density of a particular material is often a characteristic physical property of that material. Can density be used to identify materials?

Science in ACTION

Some applications of density in our everyday lives are shown below.

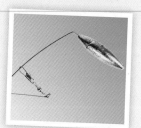

High density materials such as lead are used to make sinkers in fishing rods.

Composite materials with low densities are used to make aeroplanes.

Try This!

1. Collect a cupful of water from the tap.

2. Measure the mass and volume of the water.

3. Find the density of the tap water. Is the tap water pure water? Why?

Strength

The **strength** of a material is its ability to support a heavy load without breaking or tearing.

Steel and concrete are strong materials used for making buildings, bridges and pavements.

Most pure metals are weak. However, they can be made stronger by combining with other metals or non-metals to form mixtures called alloys. For example, steel, which is made from a combination of iron and carbon, is much stronger than pure iron.

Apart from alloys, composite materials like fibre glass are some examples of strong materials made by scientists.

Hardness

> The **hardness** of a material is its ability to withstand scratches and wear.

A material can scratch all other materials that are softer than itself but cannot scratch those that are harder than itself.

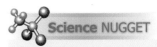

Fig. 5.6 The iron nail scratches the plastic.

Fig. 5.7 Titanium spectacle frames

Titanium is one of the hardest metals. For this reason, it is used to make aircraft, spectacle frames and artificial human bones.

Name a physical property of titanium other than its hardness that makes it suitable to make spectacle frames.

Diamond, a form of carbon, is very hard and can only be cut by other diamonds.

Graphite, another form of carbon, is soft and is widely used as pencil lead.

Fig. 5.8 Diamond

Fig. 5.9 Pencil lead

Try This!

Obtain some chalk from your neighbourhood bookstore. Find out whether chalk is harder than your fingernail by doing the following test:

1. Rub a piece of chalk on your fingernail.

2. Wipe off any marks made by the chalk. Can you see any scratches on your fingernail?

3. Next, scratch the piece of chalk with your fingernail.

4. Can you see the scratch made by your fingernail on the chalk?

5. Which substance is harder – the chalk or your fingernail?

Flexibility

> The **flexibility** of a material is its ability to bend without breaking.

To compare the flexibility of materials, the setup shown below can be used.

The larger the weight needed to bend a material to a certain distance, the lesser the flexibility of the material.

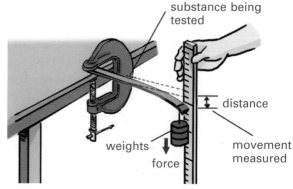

Fig. 5.10 Comparing the flexibility of different materials

Science NUGGET

Substances such as ceramics which are not flexible are called rigid.

Substances such as glass which can break easily when bent are termed brittle.

Some examples of objects which use flexibility are shown below.

Fig. 5.11 A flexible curve is used to draw curves.

Fig. 5.12 A pole vault must be flexible to help athletes leap over the bar.

Electrical Conductivity

Science in ACTION

> The **electrical conductivity** of a material is a measure of how readily an electric current flows through the material.

Materials that allow electric current to flow through them easily are classified as **electrical conductors**. Metal and carbon are examples of good electrical conductors.

An electric wire is made up of copper wires that conduct electric current and a rubber coating to insulate the electric current and stop it from flowing out of the copper wires.

Materials that do not allow large electric currents to flow through them easily are classified as **electrical insulators**. Non-metals, with the exception of carbon, are good electrical insulators. Can good electrical insulators be termed as poor electrical conductors?

Can you name some electrical conductors and insulators?

Fig. 5.13 Why do electricians often wear rubber gloves and shoes?

▶**Activity 14 P.B.**

Thermal Conductivity

> The **thermal conductivity** of a material is a measure of how readily heat flows through the material.

Place your hand on a metal pole. Does your hand feel cold? This is because metal is a type of material that allows heat from your hand to flow through it easily. We call this kind of material **thermal conductor**. Are metals the only thermal conductors?

Place your hand on a plastic pole. Does your hand feel as cold? Plastic belongs to a class of materials called **thermal insulators**, which do not allow heat to flow through them easily. In general, gases and non-metallic materials like wood are good thermal insulators. What do you think is the best thermal insulator?

Metal

Ceramic

Glass

Plastic

Fig. 5.14 Which are thermal conductors and which are thermal insulators?

Fig. 5.15 Does ice-cream have a fixed melting point?

Melting Point

The **melting point** of a substance is the temperature at which the substance changes from solid to liquid.

For example, the melting point of pure ice at 0 °C implies that ice changes into water at 0 °C.

The melting points of metals are usually very high. For example, iron has a melting point of 1 539 °C while gold has a melting point of 1 063 °C.

Compare the melting points of metals and water. From your observations of the surroundings, is there any evidence to show that most metals have very high melting points? Which is the one metal that is a liquid at room temperature? What is it used for?

Like density, melting point is a characteristic physical property of substances.

Suppose there is an alloy of iron and gold. Do you think this alloy will have a specific melting point? What will you observe if this alloy is heated to a temperature of 1 063 °C?

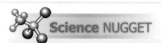

The boiling point of water placed in a pressure cooker is increased by the high pressure of gases trapped in the pressure cooker.

Boiling Point

The **boiling point** of a substance is the temperature at which the substance changes from liquid to gas.

For example, the boiling point of pure water at 100 °C implies that water changes into steam at 100 °C.

Boiling point is also a characteristic physical property of a substance.

Compare the boiling points of water and gases like oxygen or nitrogen – which is lower? How do you know?

Some refineries separate mixtures into their components by using the different boiling points of the components. You will learn how it is done in Chapter 7 (Separation Techniques).

5.3 Distinguishing Among the Main Classes of Materials

Note the amount of objects we throw away every day.

Fig. 5.16 Some materials we throw away every day

These objects are made of different types of materials. Why should we reduce the amount of materials used or disposed of? How are we going to do that?

To start with, we should first understand the properties of the different materials. Scientists have classified materials into five main classes based on their common properties:

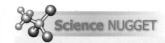

Science NUGGET

Recycling is a way to manage waste in the world. To make the process of recycling easier, objects to be thrown away are first put into different bins like the one shown below.

Recyclable materials include glass, paper, aluminum and iron. Food and garden waste can also be recycled with the help of micro-organisms.

Physical property	Metal	Non-metal			
		Ceramic	**Glass**	**Plastic**	**Fibre**
Density	Very high	High	High	Low	Low
Strength	Very high	Fair	Fair	Fair	Low
Hardness	Very hard	Hard	Fairly hard	Soft	Soft
Flexible?	Yes	No	No	Moderate	Yes
Electrical Conductivity	Good	Poor	Poor	Poor	Poor
Thermal Conductivity	Good	Poor	Good	Poor	Poor
Melting Point	Very high	High	High	Low	Combustible
Malleability	Malleable	Brittle	Brittle	Brittle	Brittle
Ductile?	Yes	No	No	No	Yes
Opaque?	Yes	Yes	No	Yes for some	Yes
Corrodes easily?	Yes for some	No	No	No	Yes, under damp/acidic conditions

Table 5.1 Some materials and their properties

5.4 Choosing the Right Materials

Most of our everyday objects are made up of more than one material. How would you choose a suitable material to make a part of an object? It all depends on the properties of the materials.

Let us take the light bulb for example. Study the functions of the different parts of a light bulb, the choice of materials and their related properties.

Glass bulb
Function   : To allow light to pass through
Material   : Glass
Related
properties : Transparent,
               electrical insulator

Filament (a very thin resistance wire)
Function   : To produce light when heated
Material   : Metal
Related
properties : Electrical conductor,
               very high melting point,
               ductile, malleable

Connecting and supporting wires
Function   : To provide support to
               the filament
Material   : Metal
Related
properties : Electrical conductor,
               very high melting point,
               ductile, malleable

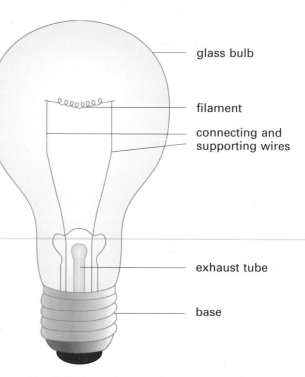

Fig. 5.17 Incandescent lamp

glass bulb

filament

connecting and
supporting wires

exhaust tube

base

Exhaust tube
Function   : To provide support to filament
               and connecting wires
Material   : Ceramic
Related
properties : High melting point,
               electrical insulator,
               heat insulator, strong

Base
Function   : To connect the bulb to
               the power source
Material   : Metal
Related
properties : Electrical conductor,
               malleable

▶ Activity 5.2 T.W.

Besides physical properties, other factors to consider when deciding if a material is suitable for certain uses would include its cost, appearance and chemical properties. Should we also consider probable moral and social issues when choosing a material?

Exploring Further

Use your knowledge of the properties of different materials to explain why they should or should not be used in the following objects:

(a)   electrical wires made of silver
(b)   school uniforms made of wool
(c)   plastic bags made of non-biodegradable material
(d)   test tubes made of porcelain

Key Points

1.   A set is a group of objects which share one or more similar properties.

2.   Classification is the grouping of objects into sets according to one or more common properties.

3.   There are many ways of classifying the same group of objects.

4.   A physical property is any aspect of an object or substance that can be measured without changing its identity.

5.   The following are some physical properties of materials:

Physical Property	What it means
Density	Mass per unit volume
Strength	Ability to support a heavy load without breaking or tearing
Hardness	Ability to withstand scratches and wear
Flexibility	Ability to bend without breaking
Electrical Conductivity	A measure of how readily an electric current flows through
Thermal Conductivity	A measure of how readily heat flows through
Melting Point	The temperature at which a substance changes from solid to liquid
Boiling Point	The temperature at which a substance changes from liquid to gas

6.   Materials can be classified into five main classes such as metals, glass, ceramics, plastics and fibres.

7.   Different materials have different properties that make them suitable for use in certain objects to serve particular functions.

1. How does the classification of materials

   a) benefit us;

   b) help in our study of science;

   c) affect our environment?

2. Write down three physical properties of the following materials:

   a) Ceramics

   b) Glass

   c) Plastics

   d) Fibres

   e) Metals

3. Classify the following materials in as many ways as you can. State how you have classified them.
   diamond, quartz, iron, graphite, copper, glass, plastics, rubber, cotton, aluminium

4. Name the main class of materials you would use to make the products listed below.
   Justify your choice by relating the properties of the chosen materials to their uses.

   (a) Chair

   (b) Pyjamas

   (c) Flower pot

   (d) Food wrap

   (e) Drink can

   (f) Electric plug cover

▶**Revision 5 T.W.**

At a GLANCE

Complete the following concept map for this chapter.

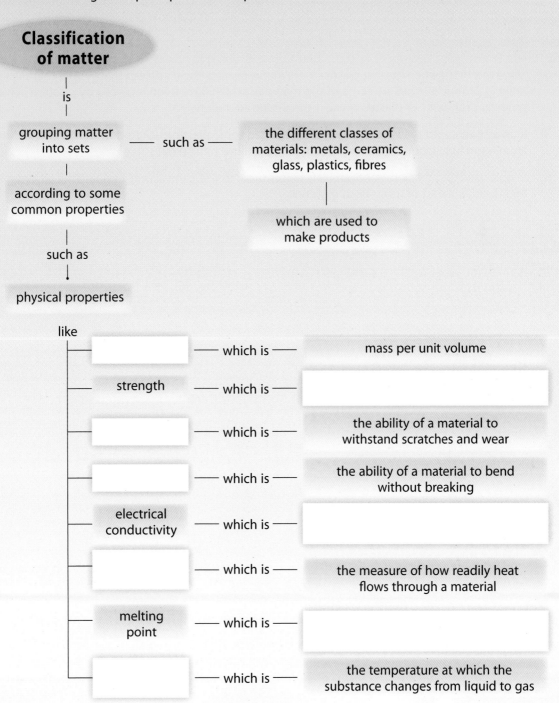

Classification of matter

is

grouping matter into sets ——— such as ——— the different classes of materials: metals, ceramics, glass, plastics, fibres

according to some common properties

which are used to make products

such as

physical properties

like

—— which is —— mass per unit volume

strength —— which is ——

—— which is —— the ability of a material to withstand scratches and wear

—— which is —— the ability of a material to bend without breaking

electrical conductivity —— which is ——

—— which is —— the measure of how readily heat flows through a material

melting point —— which is ——

—— which is —— the temperature at which the substance changes from liquid to gas

Classify the materials that are used to make a mountain bike and present it in the form of a chart.

1. A composite material is made from two or more materials combined together so that the new material has the properties of the combined materials. An example is fibreglass, which is made from glass fibres embedded in plastics. In what ways is a fibreglass boat superior to one made from wood?

2. Since the 1850s when the first plastics were made, plastics have replaced many other materials in making products. What are some of the materials which have been replaced by plastics? Which physical properties of plastics make it the preferred material?

3. If an archaeologist tells you that he has unearthed some plastic buckets and trinkets made from aluminium in ancient civilisation sites, will you believe him? Why?

4. People used to carry cloth handkerchiefs before facial tissues came along. Evaluate the advantages and disadvantages of using both materials.

▶**Portfolio Assessment 5 T.W.**

6

Elements, Compounds and Mixtures

In this chapter, you will learn to:

- recognise that substances can be classified as elements, compounds and mixtures

- identify elements as the basic building blocks of matter

- recognise that elements are classified according to their properties

- classify elements as metals and non-metals based on their characteristic properties

- describe compounds as substances consisting of two or more chemically combined elements

- describe mixtures as two or more elements and/or compounds that are not chemically combined

- distinguish among elements, compounds and mixtures

- show an appreciation of the systematic investigations involved in the study of substances

What produces the different beautiful colours in fireworks?

Look at the following pictures.

Pencil lead   Diamond

Fig. 6.1 Two forms of carbon

Do you know that they are made from the same substance – an element called carbon?

In this chapter, you will learn more about elements – what they are, how many types there are and how scientists classify them. We will also explore how elements can be combined to form mixtures and compounds and learn more about their characteristics.

6.1 Elements

The early Greeks believed that all matter was made up of only four substances: air, earth, fire and water.

The ancient Chinese believed that all matter was made up of five and not four substances: gold, wood, water, fire and earth.

Today, thanks to the systematic study of matter done by scientists, we know that all matter is made up of more than 110 substances!

Fig. 6.2 History of matter

All matter is made up of basic building blocks called elements.

> An **element** is a substance which cannot be split into two or more simpler substances by chemical reactions.

Elements are thus the simplest kind of matter.

While water can be broken down into simpler substances like hydrogen and oxygen, the hydrogen and oxygen cannot be broken down into simpler substances. Are water, hydrogen and oxygen elements? Why do you think so?

There are more than 110 elements, with 92 of the elements occurring naturally and the remaining ones man-made. Every element is given a name. Very often, artificial elements are named after the scientists who made them. Do you think there will be more elements in future? Why?

Each element is also given a chemical symbol. A chemical symbol is a shortened form – an abbreviation – of the name of an element. It takes one or two letters from the name of the element it represents. An element is often known by different names in different languages, but it has only one chemical symbol.

Element	Chemical symbol
Hydrogen	H
Calcium	Ca
Zinc	Zn
Iron	Fe

Table 6.1   Some elements and their chemical symbols

From Table 6.1, you will notice that:

- the first letter in a chemical symbol is always a capital letter;
- any other letter that follows is in lower case;
- the letters can come from names of the element in other languages such as Arabic, Greek and Latin (e.g. Iron, in Latin, is ferrum, hence the symbol Fe.);
- for two-letter symbols, they may not always be the first two letters of the name of the element. Can you give an example?

6.2 Classification of Elements

How do you think elements are classified? Can they be classified according to their names or symbols like how we classify books in the library in alphabetical order, or are they classified according to other criteria?

Over the years, scientists have tried to arrange the elements in an orderly manner so that we can study and understand matter more easily.

Through their years of hard work and perseverance, scientists have classified elements in a number of useful ways according to their properties. The way different scientists classify elements also depends on their individual needs and interests.

Classifying Elements in a Periodic Table

Scientists like Mendeleev who are interested in studying the chemical properties of elements, prefer to classify them into groups of similar chemical properties arranged systematically in a table called the **Periodic Table** (see Fig. 6.4 on the next page).

The unit masses of the elements are arranged in an increasing order (from left to right) and their chemical properties actually repeat in a periodic manner!

For example, the elements in the last column (helium, neon, etc.) share a common chemical property – they do not combine chemically with other elements. They are collectively known as inert gases.

Can you think of other ways to arrange the elements?

Fig. 6.3 Russian scientist, Dmitri Ivanovich Mendeleev

The Periodic Table of the Elements

I	II	III	IV	V	VI	VII	O
							4 **He** Helium 2

| 1 **H** Hydrogen 1 | | | | | | | |

| 7 **Li** Lithium 3 | 9 **Be** Beryllium 4 | | | | | | |
| 23 **Na** Sodium 11 | 24 **Mg** Magnesium 12 | | | | | | |

| 39 **K** Potassium 19 | 40 **Ca** Calcium 20 | 45 **Sc** Scandium 21 | 48 **Ti** Titanium 22 | 51 **V** Vanadium 23 | 52 **Cr** Chromium 24 | 55 **Mn** Manganese 25 | 56 **Fe** Iron 26 | 59 **Co** Cobalt 27 | 59 **Ni** Nickel 28 | 64 **Cu** Copper 29 | 65 **Zn** Zinc 30 |

| 85 **Rb** Rubidium 37 | 88 **Sr** Strontium 38 | 89 **Y** Yttrium 39 | 91 **Zr** Zirconium 40 | 93 **Nb** Niobium 41 | 96 **Mo** Molybdenum 42 | 99 **Tc** Technetium 43 | 101 **Ru** Ruthenium 44 | 103 **Rh** Rhodium 45 | 106 **Pd** Palladium 46 | 108 **Ag** Silver 47 | 112 **Cd** Cadmium 48 |

| 133 **Cs** Caesium 55 | 137 **Ba** Barium 56 | 139 **La** Lanthanum 57 * | 178 **Hf** Hafnium 72 | 181 **Ta** Tantalum 73 | 184 **W** Tungsten 74 | 186 **Re** Rhenium 75 | 190 **Os** Osmium 76 | 192 **Ir** Iridium 77 | 195 **Pt** Platinum 78 | 197 **Au** Gold 79 | 201 **Hg** Mercury 80 |

| 223 **Fr** Francium 87 | 226 **Ra** Radium 88 | 227 **Ac** Actinium 89 † | | | | | | | | | |

Group III–O:

III	IV	V	VI	VII	O
11 **B** Boron 5	12 **C** Carbon 6	14 **N** Nitrogen 7	16 **O** Oxygen 8	19 **F** Fluorine 9	20 **Ne** Neon 10
27 **Al** Aluminium 13	28 **Si** Silicon 14	31 **P** Phosphorus 15	32 **S** Sulphur 16	35.5 **Cl** Chlorine 17	40 **Ar** Argon 18
70 **Ga** Gallium 31	73 **Ge** Germanium 32	75 **As** Arsenic 33	79 **Se** Selenium 34	80 **Br** Bromine 35	84 **Kr** Krypton 36
115 **In** Indium 49	119 **Sn** Tin 50	122 **Sb** Antimony 51	128 **Te** Tellurium 52	127 **I** Iodine 53	131 **Xe** Xenon 54
204 **Tl** Thallium 81	207 **Pb** Lead 82	209 **Bi** Bismuth 83	**Po** Polonium 84	**At** Astatine 85	**Rn** Radon 86

Lanthanoid series:

| 140 **Ce** Cerium 58 | 141 **Pr** Praseodymium 59 | 144 **Nd** Neodymium 60 | **Pm** Promethium 61 | 150 **Sm** Samarium 62 | 152 **Eu** Europium 63 | 157 **Gd** Gadolinium 64 | 159 **Tb** Terbium 65 | 162 **Dy** Dysprosium 66 | 165 **Ho** Holmium 67 | 167 **Er** Erbium 68 | 169 **Tm** Thulium 69 | 173 **Yb** Ytterbium 70 | 175 **Lu** Lutetium 71 |

Actinoid series:

| 232 **Th** Thorium 90 | **Pa** Protactinium 91 | 238 **U** Uranium 92 | **Np** Neptunium 93 | **Pu** Plutonium 94 | **Am** Americium 95 | **Cm** Curium 96 | **Bk** Berkelium 97 | **Cf** Californium 98 | **Es** Einsteinium 99 | **Fm** Fermium 100 | **Md** Mendelevium 101 | **No** Nobelium 102 | **Lr** Lawrencium 103 |

*58–71 Lanthanoid series
†90–103 Actinoid series

Key

a	
X	
b	

a = relative atomic mass
X = atomic symbol
b = proton (atomic) number

The volume of one mole of any gas is 24 dm³ at room temperature and pressure (r.t.p.).

Fig. 6.4 The Periodic Table of the Elements

Classifying Elements by State

A simpler way to classify the elements is by observing their physical properties at room temperature.

Lead (solid)   Mercury (liquid)   Chlorine (gas)

Fig. 6.5 Comparing lead, mercury and chlorine

Study the Periodic Table (Fig 6.4). Carbon is an element that exists commonly as a solid while nitrogen is an element that exists commonly as a gas. Share with your class any other elements you know that exist commonly as solids or as gases, and verify the information with your teacher. Can you see where all the solids are located in the Periodic Table? What about the gases?

Classifying Elements as Metals and Non-metals

Locate the zigzag line shown in the Periodic Table. This line divides the elements into metals and non-metals. Are the elements to the left of the line (coloured pink) classified as metals or non-metals? How do you know?

Metallic elements are all solids at room temperature, except for mercury. Out of the 22 non-metallic elements, only ten are solids at room temperature. Name all of them. Can the state of matter be one of the characteristic properties used to classify elements into metals or non-metals?

Table 6.2 lists the characteristic properties that are used to classify elements into metals and non-metals.

Metal	Non-metal
• Shiny appearance	• Dull appearance
• High density	• Low density
• High melting point	• Low melting point
• Good electrical conductor	• Poor electrical conductor
• Good heat conductor	• Poor heat conductor
• Ductile	• Non-ductile
• Malleable	• Brittle
• Sonorous	• Non-sonorous

Table 6.2   Characteristic properties of metals and non-metals

▶Activity 15 P.B.

Using metals

Gold is used to make jewellery and ornaments because of its shiny appearance.

Aluminium is used to make aircraft bodies because it is light and resists corrosion.

Fig. 6.6 Gold jewellery   Fig. 6.7 Aircraft body made of aluminium

Iron conducts heat well and has a high melting point. Hence, it is suitable for making cooking utensils.

Silver reflects light so well that it is used to coat glass to make mirrors.

Fig. 6.8 Wok made of steel (alloy of iron and carbon)

Fig. 6.9 Mirror

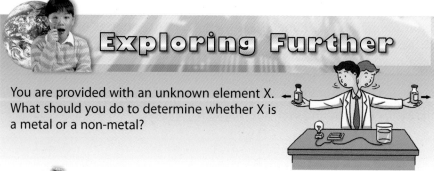

Exploring Further

You are provided with an unknown element X. What should you do to determine whether X is a metal or a non-metal?

Try This!

Name a metal and describe one of its uses. Explain how the use of the metal is related to its property or properties.

▶Activity 6 T.W.

Using non-metals

Hydrogen is used
- as rocket fuel;
- for making margarine;
- for filling weather balloons.

Fig. 6.10 Hydrogen is used as fuel in rockets.

Carbon is used
- in the formation of living tissues;
- as a fuel;
- in pencil leads.

Oxygen is used
- for respiration;
- for combustion;
- in oxy-acetylene flames for welding.

Fig. 6.11 Coloured pencil leads

Fig. 6.12 Oxy-acetylene flames for welding

The most abundant elements in our universe are hydrogen and helium. What is the most abundant element in our Earth's crust?

Fig. 6.13 Stars made of hydrogen and helium

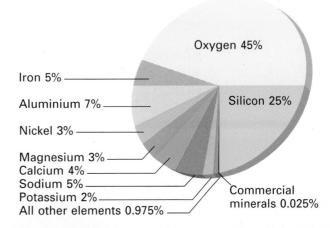

Iron 5%
Aluminium 7%
Nickel 3%
Magnesium 3%
Calcium 4%
Sodium 5%
Potassium 2%
All other elements 0.975%
Oxygen 45%
Silicon 25%
Commercial minerals 0.025%

Fig. 6.14 Composition by mass of the Earth's crust

6.3 Compounds

Can you find water in the Periodic Table? If a substance is not found in the Periodic Table, that substance is not an element.

Water is actually made of two elements - hydrogen and oxygen.

> A substance consisting of two or more different elements chemically combined together is called a **compound**.

A chemical formula is used to describe the number and type of elements that constitute a compound. For water, H_2O is the chemical formula given to it.

> **Caution!** Burning a mixture with equal volumes of hydrogen and oxygen is explosive!

Compounds are formed during chemical reactions, where heat and sometimes light energy are given out or taken in. A chemical reaction is a process in which the original substances are changed into one or more new substances.

Word equations are used to describe chemical reactions. The word equation for the formation of water from hydrogen and oxygen is written as:

$$\text{Hydrogen + oxygen} \longrightarrow \text{water}$$

Formation of Compounds

Compounds can be formed naturally or in the laboratories.

Chemical reaction between elements

When a piece of iron is exposed to oxygen, it will form a new compound, iron oxide, which is commonly known as rust.

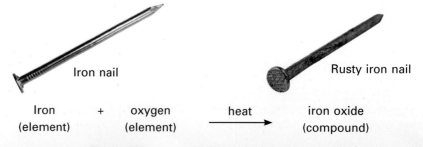

Fig. 6.15 Formation of iron oxide (rust)

▶Activity 16-17 P.B.

Chemical reaction between elements and compounds

When colourless oxygen is mixed with colourless nitric oxide, they react to produce a coloured compound, nitrogen dioxide.

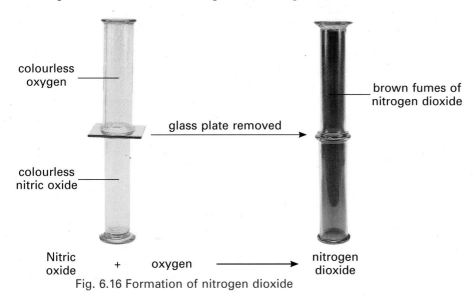

colourless oxygen

brown fumes of nitrogen dioxide

glass plate removed

colourless nitric oxide

Nitric oxide + oxygen ⟶ nitrogen dioxide

Fig. 6.16 Formation of nitrogen dioxide

Name the element(s) in the above reaction.

Chemical reaction between compounds

When black copper(II) oxide is mixed with colourless sulphuric acid, they react to produce a blue compound, copper(II) sulphate and water.

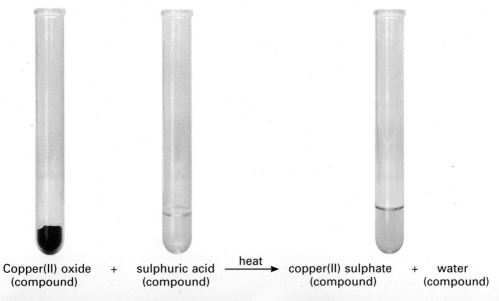

Copper(II) oxide (compound) + sulphuric acid (compound) —heat→ copper(II) sulphate (compound) + water (compound)

Fig. 6.17 Formation of copper sulphate

▶Activity 18-19 P.B.

6.4 Some Common Characteristics of Compounds

There are thousands of compounds around us, each having a different set of characteristics or properties. However, all compounds share some common properties which enable us to identify them.

- Compounds are formed by chemical reactions. During the chemical reactions, energy in the form of heat and/or light will be absorbed or given off. One example is the burning of carbon in oxygen to give carbon dioxide.

Fig. 6.18 Carbon + oxygen → carbon dioxide

- A compound has properties that are different from the properties of its constituent elements.

Fig. 6.19 Sodium + chlorine ⟶ sodium chloride

Common salt, sodium chloride, is a white crystalline solid. How is it different from its constituent elements, sodium and chlorine?

- Compounds can only be broken down into simpler substances by chemical methods such as decomposition. This normally involves heating, exposure to light or passing an electric current through them.

- The different elements in a compound are chemically combined in a fixed proportion by mass.

Fig. 6.20 Copper(II) chloride is split into solid copper and gaseous chlorine. What is used to break down the copper(II) chloride?

Fig. 6.21 1 g of hydrogen + 8 g of oxygen ⟶ 9 g of water

You will learn more about the different types of chemical reactions in Chapter 26.

6.5 Mixtures

Fig. 6.22 Mixtures do not have chemical symbols.

> A **mixture** is made up of two or more substances that are not chemically combined.

Mixtures may consist of elements, compounds or both. The substances which make up a mixture may be solids, liquids or gases.

Some Useful Mixtures

Clean air is a mixture of gaseous elements such as nitrogen, oxygen and the noble gases, as well as compounds like carbon dioxide and water vapour. Can you imagine what would happen to the green plants and animals on Earth if air just contained oxygen?

Fig. 6.23 Air

Mineral water is a mixture of water and dissolved minerals such as calcium, sodium, potassium and magnesium.

Duralumin is light and strong and is used for building aircraft bodies. It is a mixture of aluminium, copper, magnesium and manganese.

Name three harmful mixtures. State the constituents of the mixtures. How do the mixtures harm us or the environment?

Fig. 6.24 Mineral water

6.6 Some Common Characteristics of Mixtures

Table 6.3 below shows the common characteristics of mixtures. Compare them with the common characteristics of compounds.

Common characteristics of mixtures	Example
• No chemical reaction occurs during the formation of a mixture. Thus, little or no energy in the form of heat or light is given out or taken in.	Air is a mixture because no chemical reaction occurs when gases like nitrogen, oxygen, carbon dioxide, noble gases and water vapour are mixed to form air. No heat or light is taken in or given out during the formation of air.
• A mixture possesses the properties of the substances that make up the mixture.	The properties of air are those of its constituent gases. Air supports burning because oxygen in the air supports burning.
• The substances in a mixture can be mixed in any proportion by mass.	The proportion by mass of the different constituent gases in air is not constant, but can change with time and place.
• A mixture can be separated into its components by physical means such as evaporation, filtration and distillation.	Air can be separated into its different components such as nitrogen and oxygen by fractional distillation.

Table 6.3   Common characteristics of mixtures

You will learn how mixtures can be separated in Chapter 7.

Exploring Further

Why does brass have different densities?

6.7 Distinguishing Among Elements, Compounds and Mixtures

We can differentiate elements, compounds and mixtures by comparing their characteristics. Objects can be classified with the help of classification keys. The following is an example of how to distinguish whether a substance is an element, compound or mixture:

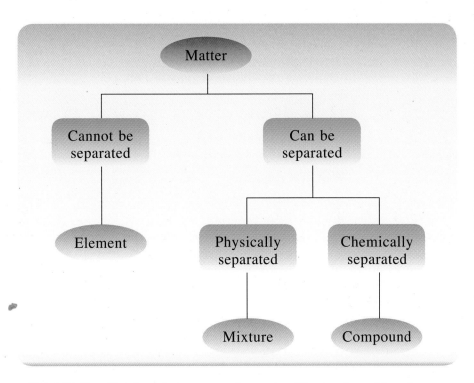

Fig. 6.25 Classification of elements using a classification branching diagram

You can use the following type of classification key too:

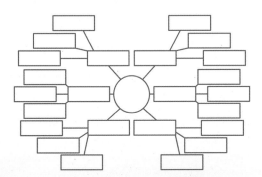

Fig. 6.26 Classification Web

Key Points

1. Elements are the basic building blocks of matter.

2. An element is a substance which cannot be split into two or more simpler substances by chemical reactions.

3. Elements can be classified in many different ways according to similar properties.

4. Elements are classified into two main groups, metals and non-metals, according to their characteristic common properties.

Metal	Non-metal
• Shiny appearance	• Dull appearance
• High density	• Low density
• High melting point	• Low melting point
• Good electrical conductor	• Poor electrical conductor
• Good heat conductor	• Poor heat conductor
• Ductile	• Non-ductile
• Malleable	• Brittle
• Sonorous	• Non-sonorous

5. A compound is a substance consisting of two or more different elements chemically combined.

6. Compounds are formed during chemical reactions where energy in the form of heat and/or light is absorbed or given off.

7. A mixture is made up of two or more substances that are not chemically combined.

8. The table below compares a compound and a mixture:

Compound	Mixture
Formed by chemical reactions	Not formed by chemical reactions
Possesses properties that are different from its constituent elements	Possesses properties of its components
Can be broken down into simpler substances by chemical methods	Can be separated into its components by physical methods
Its elements are chemically combined in a fixed proportion by mass	Its components can be mixed in any proportion by mass

9. A classification key can be used to distinguish among elements, compounds and mixtures by comparing their respective definitions and properties.

let's Review!

1. How are elements classified in the Periodic Table?

2. Describe how an unknown element is systematically investigated to determine whether it is a metal or non-metal.

3. Differentiate between compounds and mixtures.

4. State four properties of salt that make it a compound.

5. Give four reasons why salt solution is a mixture.

6. Describe how a substance is systematically investigated to determine whether it is an element, a compound or a mixture.

▶Revision 6 T.W.

Complete the following concept map for this chapter.

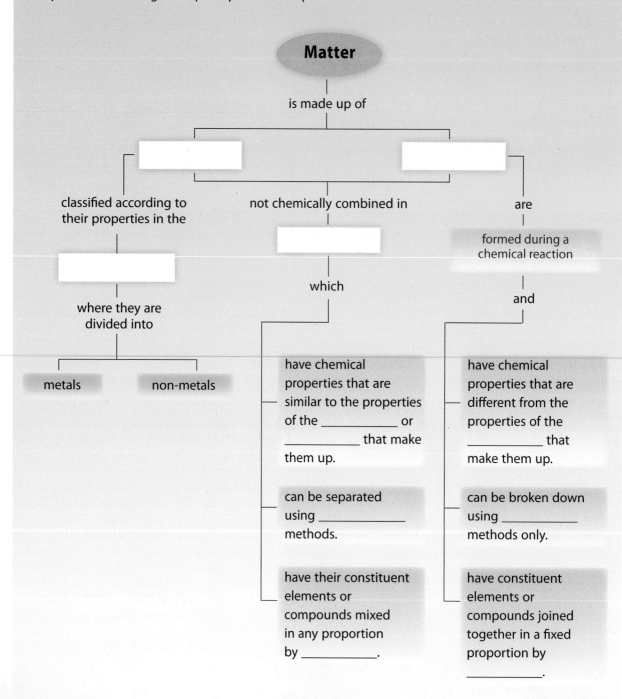

Matter

is made up of

[ ]   [ ]

classified according to
their properties in the

not chemically combined in

are

[ ]

formed during a
chemical reaction

where they are
divided into

which

and

metals   non-metals

have chemical
properties that are
similar to the properties
of the _____ or
_____ that make
them up.

have chemical
properties that are
different from the
properties of the
_____ that
make them up.

can be separated
using _____
methods.

can be broken down
using _____
methods only.

have their constituent
elements or
compounds mixed
in any proportion
by _____.

have constituent
elements or
compounds joined
together in a fixed
proportion by
_____.

Think Tank

1. A shiny element, with the chemical symbol W, has a melting point of 3 410 °C and a boiling point of 5 660 °C.

   (a) What is the physical state of this element at room temperature?

   (b) Is it common to see this element in the gaseous state? Why?

   (c) Is this element a metal or a non-metal? Explain your answer.

   (d) Name some other physical properties of this element.

   (e) With the help of the Periodic Table, find out what this element is.

2. Look around you. Note the things that are made up of only one type of element and those that are made up of combinations of different elements. Are there more of the former or latter? Explain your observation.

3. The first chemists, called alchemists, tried ways and means to create gold. In the process, they discovered many new substances and developed many procedures used in the laboratories today. However, they failed in their attempts to make gold. What do you think was the reason for their failure?

4. The substances which make up a mixture can be in any combination of the three physical states. Give an example of each of the following types of mixtures:

   (a) Solid-solid

   (b) Liquid-liquid

   (c) Gas-gas

   (d) Liquid-gas

   (e) Solid-liquid

   (f) Solid-gas

5. Flour, salt, sugar, eggs and baking powder are ingredients for baking a cake. When you mix these ingredients, you get batter. Is batter a mixture or a compound? The batter is put into an oven to bake into a cake. Is the cake a mixture or a compound? Explain your answers.

6. For a long time, water was thought to be an element until scientific breakthroughs enabled water to be broken down into hydrogen and oxygen. Why do you think water was thought to be an element for so long?

CHAPTER 7

Separation Techniques

In this chapter, you will learn to:

- show an awareness of basic principles involved in some separation techniques such as filtration, distillation and paper chromatography

- explain how the properties of constituents are used to separate them from a mixture using magnetic attraction, filtration, evaporation, distillation and paper chromatography

- show an awareness of the applications of the various separation techniques in everyday life and industries

- show an awareness of the techniques involved in obtaining pure water from seawater in desalination plants (e.g. distillation and reverse osmosis)

- use separation techniques such as filtration, distillation and paper chromatography

- show an appreciation of the systematic investigations involved in the study of substances

- show an appreciation that water is a precious resource and that there is a need to conserve it

How does a water filter make our tap water cleaner at home?

In the previous chapter, we learnt that mixtures can be separated by physical methods. In this chapter, we will learn more about these separation techniques and how we use them in everyday life.

Fig. 7.1 Drying clothes in the Sun
Fig. 7.2 Filtering of dirt in a vacuum cleaner
Fig. 7.3 Separating gold

We dry our clothes in the Sun so that water will be evaporated from the clothes (separation by evaporation). The vacuum cleaner separates dirt by using a filter to trap the dirt from the air (separation by filtration). Gold can be separated from magnetite, a main constituent of black sands, by using a magnet (separation by magnetic attraction).

To separate the constituents in a mixture, we must first find a difference in the properties of the constituents that make up the mixture.

Fig. 7.4 Mixture of sulphur powder and iron filings

Is there a difference in the properties of sulphur and iron? Can we separate sulphur from iron?

If yes, we can then choose an appropriate separation technique or method which uses that difference to separate them.

Fig. 7.5 Separating a mixture of sulphur powder and iron filings into its components by removing the iron filings with a magnet

Name the separation method used to separate the mixture of sulphur and iron into its components shown in Fig. 7.5. Explain why this method was chosen. Can a box of iron nails and steel needles be separated using this method? Why?

7.1 Separation by Magnetic Attraction

If you were given a container filled with sand and iron filings, how would you separate the iron filings from the sand? The following Fig. 7.6 will show you how to do it.

Fig. 7.6 How to separate a mixture of sand and iron filings

Iron filings are made of a magnetic material, iron. It is thus possible to remove the iron filings from the mixture. Why do you think the magnet is wrapped in paper?

> Separation by **magnetic attraction** is a process in which a magnet is used to separate objects made of magnetic materials from those made of non-magnetic materials.

Some examples of magnetic materials are iron, nickel, cobalt and steel. Examples of non-magnetic materials include copper, gold and silver.

In the mining industry, magnetic separation is used to separate magnetic materials like iron from non-magnetic materials.

For example, copper ore that contains iron is crushed and then passed along a conveyor belt near strong magnets so that the iron will be attracted to the magnets and be separated from the copper (Fig. 7.7).

Magnetic separation is also used to separate iron or steel from scrap metal. Why are strong magnets often seen in junkyards?

Science in ACTION

In hospitals, a magnet is often used to remove iron splinters from a patient's eye. Can this treatment be classified as a separation technique using magnetic separation? Explain your answer.

Fig. 7.7 Using a magnet to separate iron from non-magnetic materials

Exploring Further

Find out more about magnetic separation used in the following processes:

(a) Cleaning up agricultural products like sugar

(b) Treatment of sewage

Discuss and share your findings with your class.

7.2 Separation by Filtration

Science NUGGET

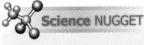

The hair in our nose filters solid particles like dust from the air we breathe in. Our kidneys filter waste products like urea and ammonium compounds from the blood that flows through them.

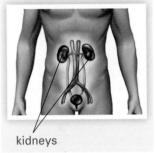

kidneys

Fig. 7.8 Straining tea Fig. 7.9 Draining water from fruits

Some of us use the above process to separate insoluble solids from a liquid. Notice that a filter is used to collect the insoluble solid.

Filtration is used to separate insoluble solids from a liquid in a solid-liquid suspension.

In the process of filtration, the insoluble solid particles are trapped in the filter as **residue** while the liquid passes through the filter and is collected as **filtrate**.

In a laboratory, a piece of filter paper fitted in a funnel is used to filter a mixture (Fig. 7.10).

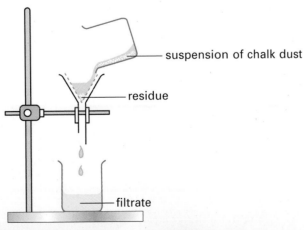

— suspension of chalk dust

— residue

— filtrate

Fig. 7.10 Filtration using filter paper. Name the residue and the filtrate.

▶Activity 20 P.B.

In a water treatment plant, raw water is filtered using sand filters. The suspended solid particles present in the raw water are trapped in the sand while the clear water runs through. However, the clear water needs to be treated further before the water becomes potable. Why?

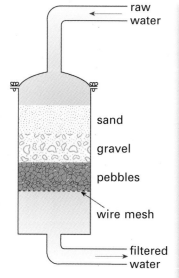

Fig. 7.11 Raw water is filtered using sand filters.

raw water

sand

gravel

pebbles

wire mesh

filtered water

Fig. 7.12 Water purification plant

Exploring Further

Find out more about how filtration is used in the following devices:

(a) Vacuum cleaner

(b) Air filter in air-conditioner

(c) Oil and air filters in cars

(d) Sieve

7.3 | Separation by Evaporation

In some countries, salt is obtained by evaporating seawater trapped in salt pans (Fig. 7.13). Heat from the Sun gradually evaporates the water in the pans, leaving the salt behind.

Evaporation is used to separate dissolved solids known as solutes from a liquid or solvent in a solid-liquid solution.

In the process of evaporation, a solution is heated so that the liquid or solvent in the solution will evaporate and leave the dissolved solids or solutes behind as residue.

Fig. 7.13 Sea salt trapped in salt pans

Two types of evaporation techniques commonly used in school laboratories are shown below.

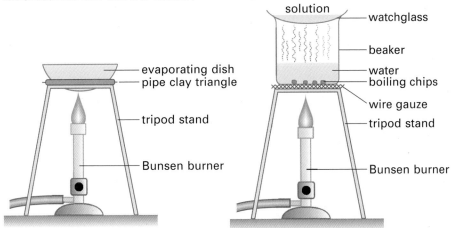

Fig. 7.14 Boiling to dryness
(Rapid evaporation technique)

Fig. 7.15 Evaporation using a steam bath (Slower evaporation technique)

The rapid evaporation technique (Fig. 7.14) is used when the solute left behind is not easily decomposed under temperatures higher than 100 °C, while the slower evaporation technique (Fig. 7.15) is used when the solute is unstable and will decompose easily at temperatures higher than 100 °C.

Can all dissolved solids be separated from a liquid in a solid-liquid mixture by evaporation? Let's find out.

Observe the effects of heating sugar as shown in Fig. 7.16. Can sugar be separated from its solution by evaporation? Why?

Fig. 7.16 Sugar decomposes on heating.

7.4 Separation by Distillation

> **Distillation** is used to separate a solvent from a solution. It can also be used to separate solutions of two liquids based on the differences in their boiling points.

In the process of distillation, a solution is heated so that its liquid component or solvent boils and subsequently escapes as a vapour. The vapour is then cooled and condensed into a liquid called **distillate**.

The diagram below shows the laboratory apparatus used for distillation.

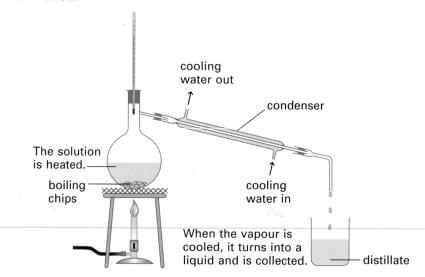

cooling water out

condenser

The solution is heated.

boiling chips

cooling water in

When the vapour is cooled, it turns into a liquid and is collected.

distillate

Fig. 7.17 Distillation

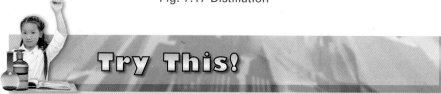

Try This!

1. Design and build your own 'solar still', to produce fresh water from seawater. One possible design is shown in the diagram below.

2. Test your 'solar still' to see if it works.

3. Suggest why the 'solar still' is sometimes included in survival kits for sailors.

small stone
clear plastic wrap
container
plastic dishpan
seawater
rocks
fresh water

7.5 Separation by Paper Chromatography

The next time you buy a packet of candy, read the label behind the package carefully.

What is meant by the term 'permitted food colourings'? How do we identify the types of food colourings used in a food sample?

contains permitted colors.

Fig. 7.18 A packet of candy that contains food colourings

Paper chromatography is commonly used to separate and identify the different coloured components in mixtures such as dyes and inks.

Paper chromatography works on the fact that all components in a mixture dissolve to different extents in the same solvent. Components which are more soluble in a solvent travel faster and further on the chromatography paper. Different coloured components will appear at different locations on the paper because they travel at different rates (Fig. 7.19).

Chromatography has many applications in the industry. Some examples are shown below.

Separating and identifying the coloured pigments in flowers and dyes

Solving crimes by finding out the type of ink used in forged cheques or counterfeits

Fig. 7.20 Applications of chromatography in the industry

Fig. 7.19 Rings formed by the different coloured components. How many coloured components are there?

Science NUGGET

Colourless substances can also be analysed using paper chromatography. To analyse colourless substances such as sugars, the mixture is first separated using paper chromatography. The paper is then sprayed with a chemical compound that reacts with the sugar to produce coloured spots which can be easily identified.

Science in ACTION

The Chemical and Microbiological Test Centre of the Singapore Productivity and Standards Board often conducts random checks on samples of processed food to ensure that only permitted food colourings and flavours are present in the food.

▶Activity 21 P.B.   ▶Activity 7.1 T.W.

Singapore is surrounded by water but yet is one of the most water-scarce countries in the world. Why?

Over the years, Singapore has tried various ways and means to be self-sufficient in its water supply. Besides importing water from other countries, what other ways is Singapore increasing her water supply?

As a Singapore citizen, how can you play a part?

7.6 Obtaining Pure Water from Seawater

Singapore opened her first desalination plant in Tuas in 2005.

Drinking water is obtained from seawater by removing its salt and other waste particles. This process is called **desalination**. Distillation and reverse osmosis are two separation techniques used in desalination plants to purify seawater.

Distillation

The distillation process in the desalination plant is similar to the one described in Section 7.4 on page 100.

$$\text{Seawater} \xrightarrow[\text{boiling}]{\text{undergoes}} \text{steam (water vapour)} \xrightarrow[\text{condensation}]{\text{undergoes}} \text{fresh water}$$

Although the process of distillation is simple, it requires a lot of heat. This heat comes mainly from the burning of fossil fuels, and so desalination using distillation is often very expensive.

Why do you think solar desalination plants using distillation are able to produce cheaper fresh water?

Reverse Osmosis

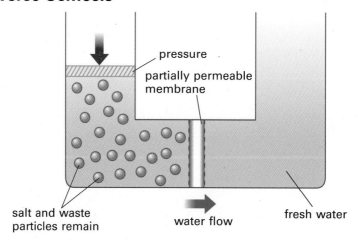

Fig. 7.21 Reverse Osmosis System. Is reverse osmosis a form of filtration?

Another method used in desalination plants is **reverse osmosis**. During this process, pressurised seawater is forced through a partially permeable membrane.

The partially permeable membrane allows fresh water to pass through it but not the dissolved salt or other waste particles. In this way, fresh water is obtained from seawater.

Exploring Further

Compare the membrane mentioned in Fig. 7.21 and the filter paper normally used in the school laboratory. What is the main difference between them? What additional feature(s) do you think a membrane suitable for reverse osmosis must have?

7.7 Obtaining Pure Water from Used Water - NEWater

Fig. 7.22 Bottles of NEWater

In Singapore, NEWater is high grade water that is purified from used water.

Used water undergoes many processes to become NEWater:

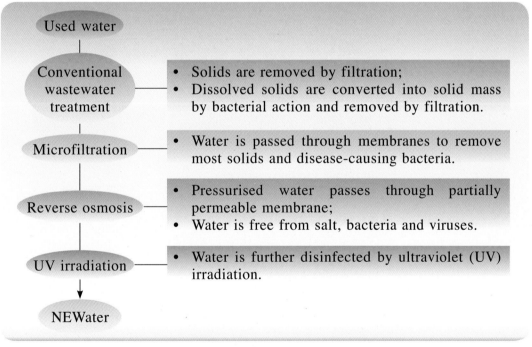

Fig. 7.23 Purification of used water to obtain NEWater

At the moment, only a small percentage of NEWater is blended with raw water in our reservoir. Although NEWater is clean water, it is not introduced into our taps directly. Would you drink NEWater directly? Why?

▶ Activity 7.2 T.W.

Key Points

1. Magnetic attraction, filtration, evaporation, distillation and paper chromatography are some separation techniques.

2. Magnetic attraction is used to separate magnetic objects from non-magnetic objects.

3. Filtration is used to separate insoluble solids from the liquid in a solid-liquid mixture. The trapped solid in the filter is called the residue. The liquid that passes through the filter is called the filtrate.

4. Evaporation is used to separate dissolved solids or solutes from the solvent in a solution provided that the dissolved solids do not change chemically on heating.

5. Distillation is used to separate a solvent from a solution.

6. Paper chromatography is used to separate and identify different coloured components in a mixture.

7. Two techniques used in desalination plants are distillation and reverse osmosis.

Let's Review!

1. Complete the following table.

Separation technique	Application
	To obtain nickel coins from a mixture of copper coins and nickel coins
	To obtain salt from seawater
	To obtain pure water from tap water
	To separate soya bean milk from soya beans
	To identify food colourings in biscuits

2. Name one household or industrial application of each of the following separation techniques:
   (a) Distillation
   (b) Evaporation
   (c) Filtration
   (d) Magnetic attraction
   (e) Paper chromatography

3. (a) What is desalination?
   (b) Why is desalination important to some countries like Singapore?
   (c) Name two techniques that are commonly used in desalination plants. What are the differences between the two techniques?
   (d) Name a technique that is currently used in Singapore's desalination plants. What are the advantages and disadvantages of using this technique?

▶Revision 7 T.W.

Complete the following concept map for this chapter.

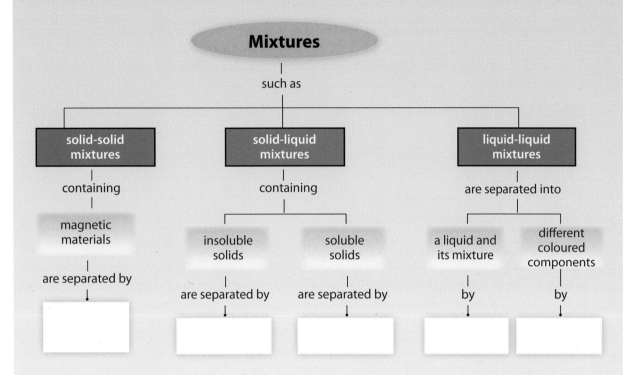

Mixtures

such as

solid-solid mixtures   solid-liquid mixtures   liquid-liquid mixtures

containing   containing   are separated into

magnetic materials   insoluble solids   soluble solids   a liquid and its mixture   different coloured components

are separated by   are separated by   are separated by   by   by

Draw another concept map for the different methods of separation.

Think Tank

1. Soaps and detergents separate grease from surfaces such as skin, walls and floors. Do soap and detergent make use of any of the separation techniques you have learnt in their cleansing actions? Do you think they use physical means or other means to remove grease?

2. Chromatography is a very useful separation technique. Suggest how it may be used in:

   (a) determining whether a sports competitor should be disqualified from a competition;

   (b) deciding whether a batch of vegetables is fit for consumption.

3. Different factors affect the rate of evaporation. From the following observations, deduce what these factors are.

   (a) A plate of water left on a table dries up faster than the same amount of water in a glass placed next to it.

   (b) Water in warm tropical rainforests evaporates more quickly than water in cooler temperate forests.

   (c) Water evaporates faster in a windy place than in a place where the air is still.

4. Study the diagram of the chromatogram. It shows four different dyes P, Q, R and S and the dyes present in a food sample X. Which of the dyes P, Q, R and S are present in the food sample X?

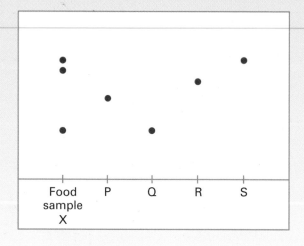

CHAPTER 8

Solutions and Suspensions

In this chapter, you will learn to:

- distinguish among solutes, solvents and solutions

- deduce the nature of solutions and suspensions by simple laboratory tests

- investigate the factors that affect the solubility and rate of dissolving of substances

- show an awareness of the importance of factors that affect the solubility and rate of dissolving of substances in homes and industries

- show an understanding that indicators are substances that change colour when an acid or alkali is added to them

- investigate the effect of a variety of acidic, alkaline and neutral solutions on Universal Indicator paper and natural indicators

- investigate the effect on Universal Indicator paper when acidic and alkaline solutions are mixed

- investigate the properties of acidic and alkaline solutions

- show an appreciation of scientific attitudes such as objectivity and accuracy in investigations on solubility and pH

Why does orange juice sometimes taste sour?

We use solutions and suspensions in our daily activities.

Maple syrup is a thick sugary solution we often take with pancakes.

Vinegar is an acidic solution that enhances the taste of food.

Alkali solution is added when making noodles to give them an elastic texture.

Some medicines exist as suspensions.

Fig. 8.1 Some applications of solutions and suspensions

What distinguishes a solution from a suspension? What are the properties of solutions like acids and alkalis?

8.1 Solutions

Most of the mixtures can be classified as solutions and suspensions.

A **solution** is a mixture in which its components are evenly mixed. It is formed when a solute dissolves in a solvent. The **solute** is the substance that dissolves, while the **solvent** is the substance that the solute dissolves in. Solvents often form the bulk of the solutions.

Fig. 8.2 Which of the mixtures shown are solutions? Why?

Let us prepare a simple solution:

- Put a teaspoon of blue copper(II) sulphate crystals into a beaker containing 100 cm³ of water and stir.

  (a) Dilute copper(II) sulphate solution

  As you stir, you will see the copper(II) sulphate crystals 'disappear' into the water to form a copper(II) sulphate solution (Fig. 8.3(a)). Can you identify the solute and solvent in the solution?

  What you have just prepared is a dilute solution. A **dilute** solution contains a small amount of solute in a large amount of solvent.

- Now add more copper(II) sulphate into the solution and stir. If you dissolve more copper(II) sulphate in the solution, the solution will become more concentrated (Fig. 8.3(b)). A **concentrated** solution contains a large amount of solute dissolved in a small amount of solvent.

  (b) Concentrated copper(II) sulphate solution

- Add more copper(II) sulphate into the solution and stir. As more copper(II) sulphate is added, you will find that it is more difficult to dissolve it. Do you know why?

  There will come a point when you cannot dissolve any more copper(II) sulphate in the solution. This solution is the most concentrated at room temperature (Fig. 8.3(c)). You have just prepared a **saturated** solution – it contains the maximum amount of dissolved solute in a given amount of solvent at a given temperature.

  copper(II) sulphate crystals

  (c) Saturated copper(II) sulphate solution

  Fig. 8.3   Copper(II) sulphate solutions of different concentrations

  How would you know whether the copper(II) sulphate solution is saturated? Is there a way to dissolve more copper(II) sulphate in a saturated solution?

A substance that dissolves in a solvent is said to be **soluble** in that solvent. A solvent does not need to be a liquid. Do you know of any solution that has a solid or gaseous solvent?

Water is known as the **universal solvent** because a large variety of substances can dissolve in it. Besides copper(II) sulphate, what else can water dissolve? A solution which has water as the solvent is known as an **aqueous solution**. Are alcoholic drinks examples of aqueous solutions?

Fig. 8.4 Alcoholic drinks

While some substances are only soluble in water, others are soluble in solvents other than water. For example, grease is soluble in petrol but is insoluble in water.

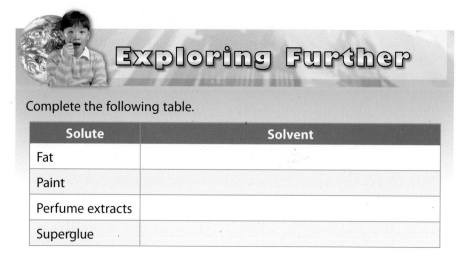

Exploring Further

Complete the following table.

Solute	Solvent
Fat	
Paint	
Perfume extracts	
Superglue	

Nature of Solutions

When a solution is formed, the tiny solute particles are mixed completely and evenly with the particles of the solvent (Fig. 8.5).

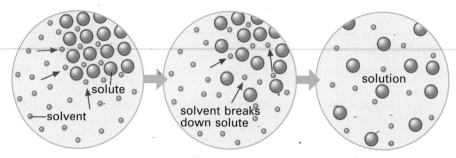

solute

solvent

solvent breaks down solute

solution

Fig. 8.5 How a solution is formed

Are the solute and the solvent particles chemically combined? Why?

A solution is **homogeneous** when its colour, density, appearance and other physical and chemical properties are the same in every part of the solution (Fig. 8.6).

When a solution is left to stand, the solute does not separate from the solvent. The solute does not settle to the bottom or float to the top.

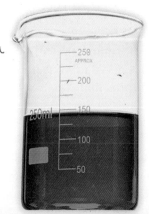

Fig. 8.6 Iodine in alcohol forms a homogeneous solution.

Shine a torch onto the copper(II) sulphate solution you prepared earlier. Does light pass through the solution like in Fig. 8.7 below?

Fig. 8.7   Light passes through a solution.

The tiny solute particles spread out evenly in the solvent. They are too small to reflect or block any light passing through the solution. This makes the solution clear or transparent.

The tiny solute particles are also small enough to pass through filter paper (Fig. 8.8). Verify this with the copper(II) sulphate solution that you have prepared.

Can filtration be used to separate a solute from its solvent in a solution? Recall the separation techniques that are commonly used to separate the solutes or solvents from solutions.

Solids, liquids and gases can all form solutions. Table 8.1 below shows some examples of the different types of solvents, solutes and solutions.

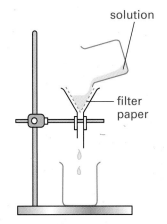

Fig. 8.8 No residue is left behind when a solution is filtered.

State of solvent	State of solute	Examples of solution
Solid	Solid	Bronze (tin dissolved in copper)
Liquid	Liquid	Amalgam (silver, tin, gold or copper dissolved in mercury)
	Solid	Sugar water (sugar dissolved in water)
	Gas	Fizzy drinks (carbon dioxide dissolved in water)
Gas	Gas	Air (oxygen, carbon dioxide, noble gases dissolved in nitrogen)

Table 8.1   Different types of solvents, solutes and solutions

8.2 Suspensions

Have you ever noticed an instruction that reads "Shake well before use" on a medicine bottle? What is the purpose of shaking the bottle before use?

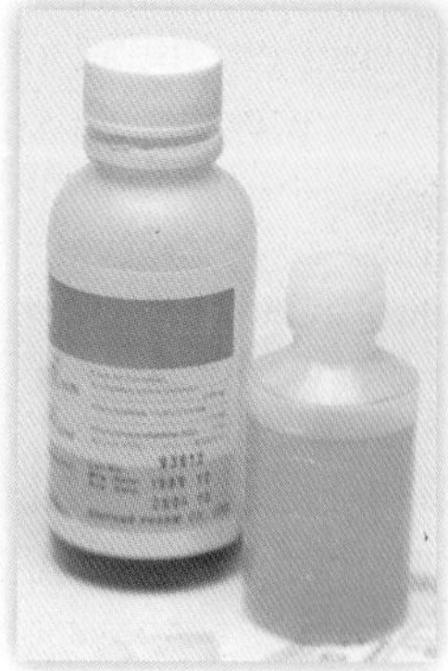

Fig. 8.9 Why is it important to read and follow all the instructions given on medicine bottles?

A **suspension** is a mixture containing insoluble solid particles suspended in a liquid. For example, chalk dust with water forms a suspension (Fig. 8.10). A suspension can also consist of liquid droplets or fine solid particles in a gas.

Fig. 8.10 A cloudy suspension of chalk dust and water

Other examples of suspensions include calamine lotion, muddy water and haze.

Fig 8.11 Calamine lotion

Fig. 8.12 A hazy environment

How does each of the above suspensions harm or benefit us?

Nature of Suspensions

When a suspension is formed, the solute often remains as large visible insoluble solid particles.

A suspension is usually cloudy. The colour, density, appearance and other physical and chemical properties of a suspension are different in every part of the suspension. This means that a suspension is **heterogeneous** (non-homogeneous).

When a suspension is left to stand for some time, the insoluble particles will float on top or settle to the bottom.

The insoluble particles in a suspension are large enough to block and prevent light from passing through the suspension, as shown in Fig. 8.13. This makes suspensions appear cloudy. How do we recognise that the insoluble particles in a suspension reflect light?

Fig. 8.13 A strong beam of light is unable to pass through a suspension.

The insoluble particles in a suspension are too large to pass through filter paper (Fig. 8.14). What is the residue left behind on the filter paper when we filter a suspension of muddy water?

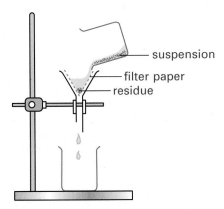

suspension

filter paper

residue

Fig. 8.14   A residue is left behind when a suspension is filtered.

Name the separation technique apart from filtration that can be used to separate the insoluble particles from a suspension.

▶Activity 22 P.B.

Another factor that affects solubility, especially for gases in liquid solvents, is pressure.

At lower pressures, the solubility of a gas in a liquid solvent decreases. This is why carbonated soft drinks fizz so much when the cap is removed.

As pressure inside the can decreases, the solubility of carbon dioxide in solution decreases and thus bubbles out as a gas.

8.3 Factors Affecting the Solubility of Substances

Solubility is the maximum amount of a solute which can dissolve in 100 g of solvent at a fixed temperature.

For example, the solubility of sugar in pure water is approximately equal to 204 g of sugar in 100 g of water at 20 °C.

Factors affecting the solubility of a solute in a solvent include the:
• nature of the solute
• nature of the solvent
• temperature of the solution

In general, the solubility of solids in liquid solvents increases with increasing temperature, but the solubility of gases in solvents decreases with increasing temperature.

In your practical lessons, you will find out how each of these factors affects the solubility of a solute.

Detergents are able to dissolve grease easily and are highly soluble in water. How does the use of a detergent with a high solubility in water help to save water?

Fig. 8.15 Detergent

8.4 Factors Affecting the Rate of Dissolving of Substances

Try This!

1. Compete with your classmates to see who will dissolve a cube of sugar in 100 cm³ of water in the shortest interval of time.

2. You may use one or more of the following to increase the rate of dissolving:

   • 100 cm³ of hot water
   • 100 cm³ of cold water
   • 100 cm³ of water at room temperature
   • spoon
   • pestle and mortar

3. Discuss and record the results in your science portfolio.

▶Activity 23-25 P.B.

Rate of dissolving is the time taken for the dissolving process, from the time the solute is added to a fixed amount of solvent, until it has completely dissolved.

Factors affecting the rate of dissolving a solute in a given volume of solvent are the:

- surface area of the solute
- temperature of the solution
- rate of stirring

In your practical lessons, you will find out how each factor affects the rate of dissolving.

Will the rate of dissolving a solute in a solvent be increased by increasing the volume of solvent ?

Applications at Home and in the Industry

Having a knowledge of the factors that affect the solubility and rate of dissolving of substances is important at home and in the industry. This is because many of the substances we use are in the form of solutes, solvents and solutions.

Fig. 8.16   A washing machine is designed to dissolve detergent efficiently.

At home, a washing machine uses hot water and a rotating drum to increase the solubility and rate of dissolving of detergent in water. Is the solubility and rate of dissolving grease in detergent also increased?

Describe another example of a household application.

In the fizzy drinks industry, the solubility and rate of dissolving of artificial flavours or extracts in water are increased by raising the temperature of the water. However, the solubility and rate of dissolving of carbon dioxide in water to form carbonated water is increased by lowering the temperature of the water or by increasing the pressure of the carbon dioxide. Why?

Describe another example of an industrial application.

Fig. 8.17   A high temperature helps to dissolve the extracts in soft drinks.

▶ Activity 26 P.B.   ▶ Activity 8 T.W

8.5 Acids and Alkalis

Acids and alkalis are two common types of aqueous solutions that we use every day. The beaker on the left contains an acid (Fig. 8.18) and the beaker on the right contains an alkali (Fig. 8.19).

Fig. 8.18   An acid

Fig. 8.19   An alkali

Can acids and alkalis be differentiated according to their appearances? Why?

Acids

Name some fruits that taste sour. What causes the sour taste of fruits?

Acids can be found all around us –

in the food we eat,

Citrus fruits

in the liquids we drink,

Tea

in our body,

Stomach secretions

and in our everyday objects.

Car battery

Fig. 8.20 Some places where acids can be found

The following table lists some of the acids that are commonly found around us.

Type of acid	Found or contained in...
Malic acid	Apples
Citric acid	Citrus fruits
Ascorbic acid	Vitamin C, most fruits and vegetables
Hydrochloric acid	Our stomach
Tannic acid	Strong tea
Lactic acid	Sour milk and yoghurt
Tartaric acid	Grapes and wine

Table 8.2   Some naturally occurring acids

Connect

Have you ever had muscle cramps while doing strenuous exercises? What causes muscle cramps?

The photograph below shows some of the acids commonly used in school laboratories.

Fig. 8.21   Some common acids found in school laboratories

The table below shows the common uses of various acids.

Name of acid	Uses
Citric acid	Making vitamins and other health salts
Ethanoic acid	Preserving food and cooking (vinegar)
Hydrochloric acid	Cleaning metal surfaces before they are coated
Nitric acid	Making fertilisers and explosives
Phosphoric acid	Making fertilisers and preventing the rusting of iron
Sulfuric acid	Making car batteries, plastics and fertilisers

Table 8.3   Some common acids and their uses

General Properties of Acidic Solutions

- Acids are generally corrosive. They can burn our skin and react with many materials including metals. They are poisonous too!

Caution!

- Always handle acids and acidic solutions with care.
- If some acid gets into your mouth, spit it out at once and rinse your mouth with plenty of water.
- If an acid comes into contact with your clothing or any other parts of your body, wash off the acid thoroughly with plenty of water.

- All acids have a sour taste.
- Acids turn blue litmus paper red.

- Aqueous solutions of acids are good electrical conductors.

Fig. 8.22 Acids turn blue litmus red.

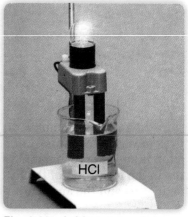

Fig. 8.23 Acids are good electrical conductors.

- Dilute acids react with reactive metals to produce hydrogen gas.

Fig. 8.24 Test for hydrogen gas

dilute hydrochloric acid	+	magnesium	→	magnesium chloride	+	hydrogen
(acid)		(metal)		(salt)		(gas)

Test for hydrogen gas

Hydrogen gas can be identified by the 'pop' sound produced when a burning splint comes into contact with the hydrogen gas.

- Dilute acids react with carbonates to produce carbon dioxide gas.

calcium carbonate	+ dilute nitric acid	→	calcium nitrate	+ water +	carbon dioxide
(carbonate)	(acid)		(salt)		(gas)

▶ Activity 27-29 P.B.

Test for carbon dioxide

Carbon dioxide gas can be identified by passing it through clear limewater. Carbon dioxide gas forms a white precipitate (suspension of a solid in a solution) when bubbled into limewater.

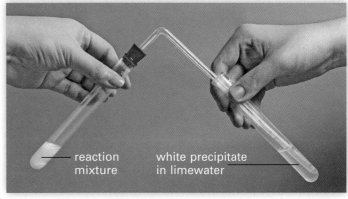

reaction mixture   white precipitate in limewater

Fig. 8.25 Test for carbon dioxide

- Acids react with alkalis to form salt and water only.

hydrochloric acid	+	sodium hydroxide	→	sodium chloride	+	water
(acid)		(alkali)		(salt)		

Alkalis

The bitter taste of some medicines like painkillers, indigestion tablets, 'milk of magnesia' and soap is caused by the alkalis they contain. All alkalis have a bitter taste.

Alkalis can also be found all around us –

in the food we eat,

in the liquids we drink,

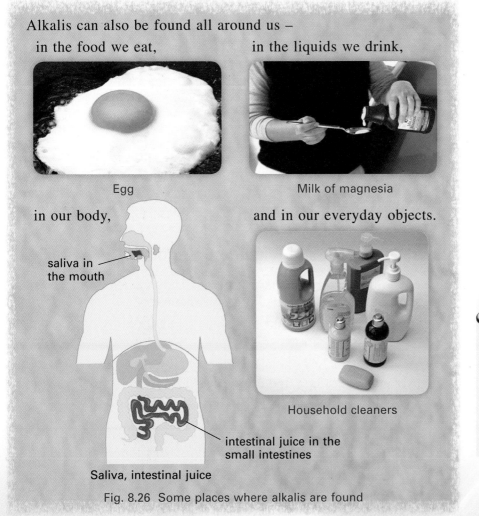

Egg

Milk of magnesia

in our body,

and in our everyday objects.

saliva in the mouth

Household cleaners

intestinal juice in the small intestines

Saliva, intestinal juice

Fig. 8.26 Some places where alkalis are found

Connect

The weak alkali contained in toothpaste is used to neutralise the acids formed by plaque bacteria on our teeth. Should mouthwash be an alkaline solution? Why?

The photograph below shows some of the alkalis commonly used in school laboratories.

Science NUGGET

The word 'caustic' is used to describe strong alkalis. For example, sodium hydroxide is known as caustic soda and potassium hydroxide as caustic potash.

Fig. 8.27 Some common alkalis found in school laboratories

The table below shows the common uses of various alkalis:

Name of alkali	Uses
Ammonia solution	Making fertilisers, bleach and cleaning liquids
Calcium hydroxide	Making mortar, reducing the acidity of soil and reducing wood shavings to pulp to make paper
Magnesium hydroxide	Making indigestion tablets and 'milk of magnesia'
Potassium hydroxide	Making paint removers and dyes for fabrics
Sodium hydroxide	Making soap, washing powders and drain cleaners

Table 8.4 Some common alkalis and their uses

General Properties of Alkaline Solutions

• Alkalis are generally corrosive liquids. They can cause bleaching. They can burn your skin and are poisonous too!

Caution!

• Always handle alkali and alkaline solutions with care.
• If some alkali gets into your mouth, spit it out at once and rinse your mouth with plenty of water.
• If an alkali comes into contact with your clothing or any other parts of your body, wash off the alkali thoroughly with plenty of water.

- All alkalis taste bitter and feel soapy.

Fig. 8.28 What makes the soap feel soapy?

- Alkalis turn red litmus paper blue.

- Alkalis are good electrical conductors.

Fig. 8.29 Alkalis turn red litmus bue.

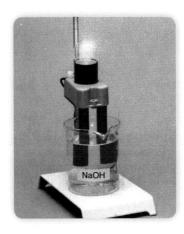

Fig. 8.30 Alkalis are good electrical conductors.

- Alkalis react with acids to form salt and water only.

potassium hydroxide + nitric acid → potassium nitrate + water
(alkali)   (acid)   (salt)

8.6 Indicators

Acidic and alkaline solutions are corrosive, so we use a suitable indicator to determine how acidic (acidity) or alkaline (alkalinity) a solution is. We have mentioned one such indicator in the previous sections – litmus paper. Which of the characteristics of litmus paper makes it a suitable indicator?

▶ Activity 30 P.B.

Try This!

Collect some of your saliva in a Petri-dish. Dip a piece of red and blue litmus paper into it. What is the colour change you observe? Is your saliva alkaline or acidic?

When mixed with a solution, an **indicator** is a substance which changes its colour according to whether the solution is acidic, alkaline or neutral. Some examples of indicators are litmus paper, Universal Indicator paper and natural indicators.

Litmus is a dye which comes from lichens, a combination of fungi and green algae growing on barks of trees. Litmus paper is made by soaking paper in litmus solution and then drying it.

Observe and compare the colour changes of the different indicators in acidic, neutral or alkaline solutions.

Indicator	Colour when solution is acidic	Colour when solution is neutral	Colour when solution is alkaline
Bromothymol blue			
Litmus			
Methyl orange			
Phenolphthalein			
Phenol red			
Universal Indicator			

pH 0 1 2 3 4 5 6 7 8 9 10 11 12 13 14

← Acidity increases   Alkalinity increases →

Fig. 8.31 Different colours of various indicators

Fig. 8.32 Universal Indicator in liquid and paper forms

How does the colour change of Universal Indicator in acidic, alkaline or neutral solutions differ from that of the other indicators?

The **Universal Indicator** is a mixture of several different types of indicators. It has the ability to show a variety of colours according to the different degrees of acidity or alkalinity of the solution mixed with it.

▶ Activity 31 P.B.

The Universal Indicator is used in either the liquid or paper form. It often comes with a colour chart. The strength of an acid or an alkali can be found by comparing the colour of the Universal Indicator in the solution against the colour chart.

Fig. 8.33 Compare the colour of the Universal Indicator against the colour chart. Is this solution acidic or alkaline?

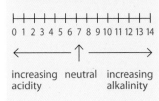

Exploring Further

When an acid is added to an alkaline solution, the acid neutralises some alkali and the solution becomes less alkaline. As more acid is added, there will come a point when the acid cancels out all the effects of the alkali and a neutral solution is obtained. Adding more acid to the neutral solution will then make the solution acidic.

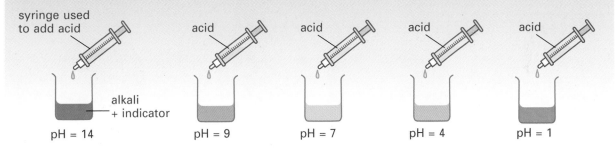

syringe used to add acid

acid   acid   acid   acid

alkali + indicator

pH = 14   pH = 9   pH = 7   pH = 4   pH = 1

The colour changes of the indicator reflect the pH of the solution.

Name a suitable indicator that can be used to show the changes in the acidity or alkalinity of the above mixture. Why is the indicator suitable?

In your practical lessons, you will investigate the effect on Universal Indicator paper when acidic and alkaline solutions are mixed.

▶Activity 32 P.B.

Study the table below which shows the changes in colour when the dyes extracted from plants are mixed with acidic or alkaline solutions.

Name of plant	Original colour of dye extracted from plant	Colour when mixed in acidic solution	Colour when mixed in alkaline solution
Coleus	Brown	Pink	Yellow
Geranium	Red	Orange	Yellow
Green spinach	Green	Yellowish green	Yellowish green
Hibiscus	Dark red	Red	Green
Marigold	Yellow	Yellow	Yellow
Periwinkle	Yellow	Pink	Yellow
Red cabbage	Purple	Pink	Green
Red spinach	Red	Pink	Yellow

Table 8.5 Colour change of plant dyes in acidic and alkaline solutions

Which plant extracts cannot be used as indicators? Why?

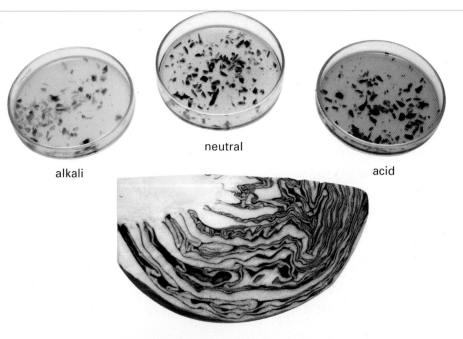

alkali

neutral

acid

Fig. 8.34 The red cabbage is an example of a natural indicator.

▶Activity 33 P.B.

Key Points

1. A solution is a homogeneous mixture that contains one or more solutes dissolved in a solvent.

2. A solution

   - is homogeneous with the same physical and chemical properties in every part of the solution;

   - allows light to pass through, making it appear clear or transparent;

   - does not leave any residue when filtered.

3. A suspension is a mixture containing insoluble solid particles suspended in a liquid. A suspension can also consist of liquid droplets or fine solid particles in a gas.

4. A suspension

   - is heterogeneous with different physical and chemical properties in different parts of the suspension;

   - prevents light from passing through, making it appear cloudy;

   - can be easily separated into filtrate and residue by filtration.

5. The solubility of a solute is the maximum amount of the solute that can dissolve in 100 g of solvent at a fixed temperature.

6. Factors affecting the solubility of a solute in a solvent include the nature of the solute, nature of the solvent and temperature of the solution.

7. The rate of dissolving a solute in a solvent depends on the rate of stirring, the temperature of the solution and the surface area of the solute.

8. Aqueous solutions can be classified as acidic, alkaline or neutral.

9. Acids

   - are usually corrosive;

   - have a sour taste;

   - turn blue litmus paper red;

   - are good electrical conductors;

   - react with reactive metals to produce hydrogen gas;

   - react with carbonates to produce carbon dioxide gas;

   - react with alkalis to form salt and water only.

10. Alkalis

   • are usually corrosive and cause bleaching;

   • have a bitter taste and feel soapy;

   • turn red litmus paper blue;

   • are good electrical conductors;

   • react with acids to form salt and water only.

11. An indicator such as litmus or Universal Indicator changes its colour when mixed with an acidic or alkaline solution.

12. Litmus is a natural indicator obtained from lichens. It turns red in acid and blue in alkali.

13. Universal Indicator is a mixture of different types of indicators. It changes colour according to the different degrees of acidity or alkalinity of the solution mixed with it.

Let's Review!

1. Distinguish between solutions and suspensions.

2. What is meant by solute, solvent and solution?

3. Name the factors that affect the solubility of a substance. Describe how each factor affects the solubility of that substance.

4. What is meant by the rate of dissolving? Describe how the rate of dissolving of a solute in a given solvent is affected by different factors.

5. Describe three uses of solvents or solutions in

   (a) homes;

   (b) industries;

   (c) agriculture;

   (d) medicine.

6. Distinguish between acids and alkalis.

7. What is the function of an indicator?

8. When would you use the Universal Indicator instead of the litmus?

▶Revision 8 T.W.

Complete the following concept map for this chapter.

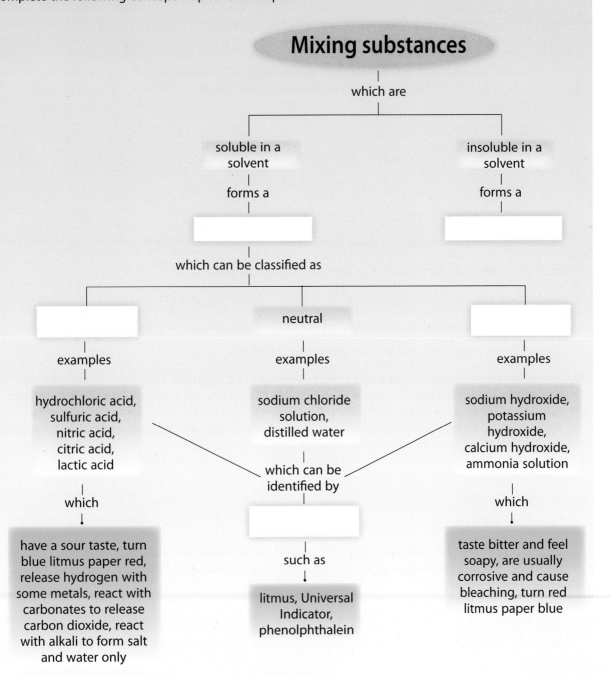

Mixing substances

which are

soluble in a solvent	insoluble in a solvent
forms a	forms a
☐	☐

which can be classified as

☐	neutral	☐
examples	examples	examples
hydrochloric acid, sulfuric acid, nitric acid, citric acid, lactic acid	sodium chloride solution, distilled water	sodium hydroxide, potassium hydroxide, calcium hydroxide, ammonia solution

which can be identified by

☐

which

have a sour taste, turn blue litmus paper red, release hydrogen with some metals, react with carbonates to release carbon dioxide, react with alkali to form salt and water only

such as

litmus, Universal Indicator, phenolphthalein

which

taste bitter and feel soapy, are usually corrosive and cause bleaching, turn red litmus paper blue

What are the similarities and differences between an acid and alkali? Show it in a concept map.

Think Tank

1. The table below shows the solubilities of some gases in a few solvents at atmospheric pressure, and at a temperature of 25 °C.

Solubility (mole percent*)

	Heptane	Benzene	Water
Hydrogen	0.069	0.026	0.0015
Nitrogen	0.12	0.45	0.0012
Methane	0.47	0.21	0.0024
Carbon dioxide	0.77	0.97	0.0608

*mole is the SI unit of amount of substance.

(a) Which of the gases above is the most soluble in water? Which is the least?

(b) Which gases are more soluble in heptane than in benzene?

(c) Draw three conclusions about the solubilities of gases from the information given in the table.

(d) What will happen to the solubilities of the gases in the solvents if the temperature is 10 °C?

(e) What are the factors that are being held constant?

2. Some substances, when mixed, do not form solutions or suspensions. They form colloids. Blood, boiled starch, aerosols and smoke are examples of colloids. When a bright source of light is shone through a colloid, e.g. boiled starch, the colloid appears very bright, yet it passes through filter paper without leaving any residue. Deduce whether colloid particles, are bigger, smaller or equal in size compared to those of

(a) solutions;

(b) suspensions.

3. (a) Suggest why normal rain water is slightly acidic.

(b) How does acid rain, formed when sulfur dioxide or oxides of nitrogen dissolve in rain water, destroy buildings and statues, especially those made from limestone (a form of calcium carbonate)?

4. You are given the following materials:
magnesium ribbons, blue litmus papers, a battery connected to a bulb and carbon electrodes, solid citric acid, aqueous solution of citric acid, solution of citric acid in propanone

Design an experiment to show that acids only exhibit acidic properties when dissolved in water.

▶**Portfolio Assessment 8 T.W.**

CHAPTER 9

Classification of Plant and Animal Life

In this chapter, you will learn to:

- show an understanding of the need to classify living organisms

- classify living organisms according to commonly observable characteristics

- classify living organisms into major taxonomic groups

- construct a dichotomous key

- use simplified dichotomous keys in identifying and classifying living organisms

- show an appreciation of the importance for Man to understand and maintain the connections among living things

- show an appreciation of Man's responsibility to have care and concern for living things and the environment

Can you tell whether this is a plant or an animal?

Study the living things – plants and animals – living around us:

Fig. 9.1 A typical pond

Fig. 9.2 A typical park

How can we tell them apart?

9.1 Classification of Living Organisms

Fig. 9.3 There are about 10 million types of living organisms.

Scientists have so far discovered about ten million different types of living organisms. They have classified these living organisms into several major taxonomic groups based on one or more similar observable characteristics and distinctive features such as body structures, development and life cycles, to make the study of living organisms easier and more systematic.

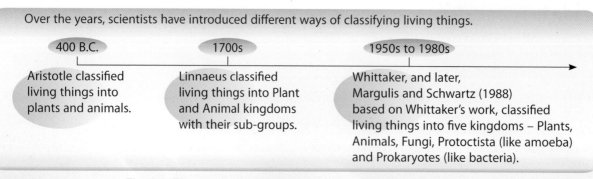

Over the years, scientists have introduced different ways of classifying living things.

400 B.C.

1700s

1950s to 1980s

Aristotle classified living things into plants and animals.

Linnaeus classified living things into Plant and Animal kingdoms with their sub-groups.

Whittaker, and later, Margulis and Schwartz (1988) based on Whittaker's work, classified living things into five kingdoms – Plants, Animals, Fungi, Protoctista (like amoeba) and Prokaryotes (like bacteria).

Fig. 9.4 The development of the classification of living things

Taxonomy refers to the process of classifying things, as well as to the study of the principles, rules and methods of classification. Living things in a major taxonomic group can be further classified into sub-groups according to common observable characteristics or traits.

The scientific name of an organism shows how it is classified. For example, the scientific name for lion is:

Panthera   *leo*

Panthera is the *genus* of the animal. This group of animals refers to large roaring cats.

leo refers to the *species* of the animal - lion.

Fig. 9.5 *Panthera leo* is the scientific name of the lion.

Fig. 9.6 shows examples of some organisms and their scientific names.

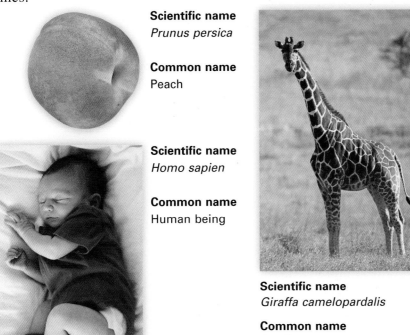

Scientific name
Prunus persica

Common name
Peach

Scientific name
Homo sapien

Common name
Human being

Scientific name
Giraffa camelopardalis

Common name
Giraffe

Fig. 9.6 Scientific names of peach, human being and giraffe

Science NUGGET

We can also classify the lion into the following groups:

- Kingdom: Animalia
  - all animals

- Phylum: Chordata
  - all vertebrate animals

- Class: Mammalia
  - all mammals

- Order: Carnivora
  - all carnivores

- Family: Felidae
  - all cats

- Genus: *Panthera*
  - the big roaring cats including lions, tigers, and leopards

- Species: *leo*
  - the lions

Notice that the classification 'Kingdom' is the most general and 'Species' is the most specific one.

Scientists use standard scientific names in the classification of living things. The use of standard scientific names ensures that different scientists around the world are referring to the same living things. This is important, especially when there is a need to identify a disease-causing organism and the use of a scientific name could mean saving lives or causing deaths!

Fig. 9.7 *Homo habilis*

9.2 Classification of Plants

Why are plants classified into different major taxonomic groups? Name the observable characteristic shown in the photographs below that is used to classify plants into two major taxonomic groups.

Fig. 9.8 Sunflower   Fig. 9.9 Fern

Science NUGGET

Rafflesia is the biggest flower on Earth. It can be found in parts of Southeast Asia, such as Borneo, Sumatra and the Philippines.

Plants can be broadly divided into two major groups: flowering plants that produce flowers, and non-flowering plants that do not produce flowers.

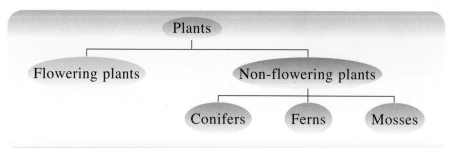

Fig. 9.10 Major taxonomic groups of plants

Do flowering plants produce flowers all the time? How can we identify a plant as a flowering plant if the plant does not produce flowers?

Different scientists often use different features of plants to classify them into groups. Study the observable characteristics of the different groups of plants in the following table.

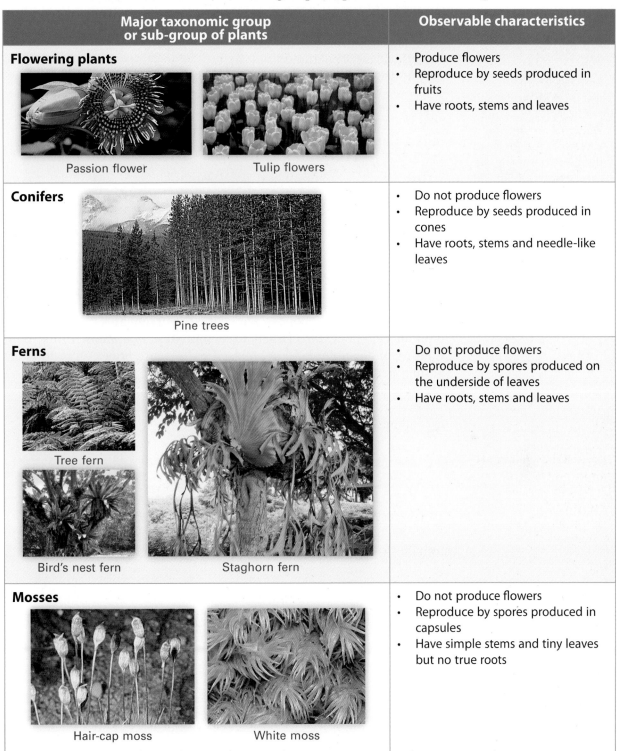

Major taxonomic group or sub-group of plants	Observable characteristics
Flowering plants Passion flower Tulip flowers	• Produce flowers • Reproduce by seeds produced in fruits • Have roots, stems and leaves
Conifers Pine trees	• Do not produce flowers • Reproduce by seeds produced in cones • Have roots, stems and needle-like leaves
Ferns Tree fern Bird's nest fern Staghorn fern	• Do not produce flowers • Reproduce by spores produced on the underside of leaves • Have roots, stems and leaves
Mosses Hair-cap moss White moss	• Do not produce flowers • Reproduce by spores produced in capsules • Have simple stems and tiny leaves but no true roots

Table 9.1 Major taxonomic groups and sub-groups of plants and their observable characteristics

Name another observable characteristic apart from producing flowers that is used to classify plants into different groups.

Exploring Further

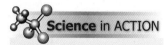
Angiosperms are plants that produce flowers and seeds enclosed in fruits. They are an important source of food for living things. For example, we eat vegetables, fruits and cereals, all of which are angiosperms. We also use technology to produce clothing and medicine from angiosperms.

Fungi such as mushrooms, toadstools and mould used to be classified as plants. Why are they now placed in a separate kingdom?

9.3 Classification of Animals

Animals with backbones are called **vertebrates** and animals without backbones are called **invertebrates**. Mammals, birds, fish, reptiles and amphibians are classified as vertebrates. Are humans vertebrates?

Animals are generally classified into the following two major taxonomic groups and sub-groups.

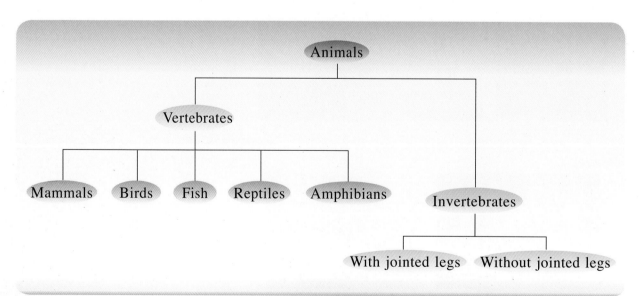

Fig. 9.11 Major taxonomic groups and sub-groups of animals

Vertebrates

Mammals

Whale

Tiger

Bat

Elephant

Monkey

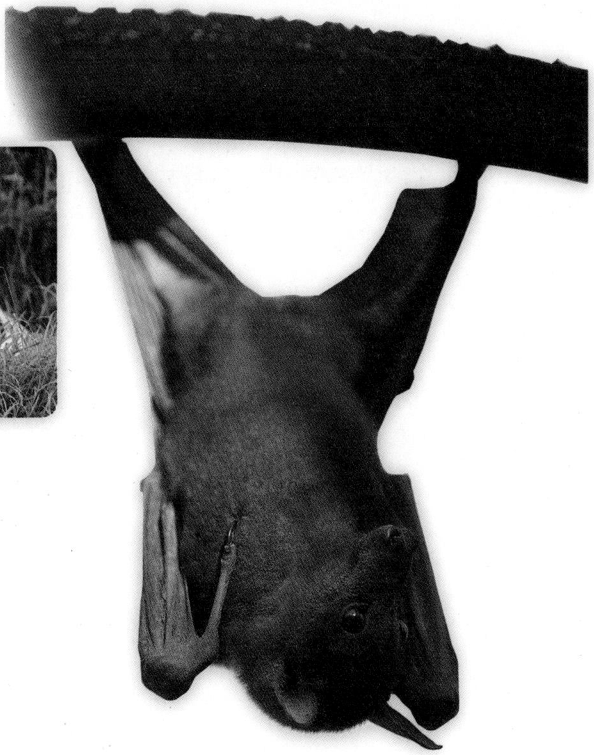

Fig. 9.12 Mammals

Mammals are warm-blooded animals as their body temperatures do not change with their surrounding temperatures. Their bodies are covered with hair or fur. Is our body covered with hair or fur? Name a mammal which has fur.

Young mammals are the only animals which feed on their mother's milk produced by mammary glands.

What do human beings have in common with the animals shown in Fig. 9.12 above?

How do mammals reproduce? All mammals, except the duck-billed platypus and the spiny anteater, reproduce by giving birth to live young.

Fig. 9.13 Duck-billed platypus

Fig. 9.14 Echidna

How do the duck-billed platypus and the spiny anteater reproduce?

Birds

Birds are warm-blooded animals which reproduce by laying eggs with shells. They have feathers, beaks and wings, but not all birds can fly. Which birds shown below do not fly?

Owl

Duck

Toucan

Ostrich

Penguins

Fig. 9.15 Birds

Are birds the only animals with feathers?

Fish

Fish are cold-blooded animals as their body temperature changes according to their surrounding temperature.

Fish are well adapted for life under water. They have gills to breathe or absorb oxygen dissolved in the water. They also have fins and tails for swimming and streamlined bodies to help them move faster.

Clownfish   Shark   Lion fish

Seahorse   Stingray   Puffer fish

Fig. 9.16 Fish

Most fish reproduce by laying eggs. How do other fish reproduce?

Reptiles

Reptiles are also cold-blooded animals that live on land. Although reptiles have lungs, they also absorb oxygen through the membranes in their mouth. They also have waterproof skins that help to retain body moisture and enable them to live in hot and dry places such as deserts.

Snake

Crocodile

Tortoise

Fig. 9.17 Reptiles

Fig. 9.18 Is the chameleon a reptile or an amphibian?

Reptiles reproduce by laying eggs on land. Their eggs have thick, hard and leathery shells to prevent them from drying up.

Fig. 9.19 Box turtle laying eggs

Young amphibians undergo a lot of changes as they grow to become adults. The process of change from young to adult is called metamorphosis.

Amphibians

Amphibians are cold-blooded animals that can live both on land and in water. Young amphibians live in water and breathe through their gills whereas the adults live on land and breathe through their lungs and skin. Amphibians usually have loose and moist skin.

Frog   Toad   Salamander   Frogs and their spawn

Fig. 9.20 Amphibians

Most amphibians spend their adult lives on land but return to the water to lay their eggs. The photo above shows the eggs or spawn laid by a frog. Compare the eggs laid by a frog to those laid by a turtle. What differences can you observe?

Invertebrates

Arthropods – Invertebrates with jointed legs

Invertebrates with jointed legs are called **arthropods**. Arthropods have segmented bodies covered with shells called **exoskeletons**. Exoskeletons are shed from time to time as the arthropod grows.

Arthropods are further divided into sub-groups according to their number of legs as follows:

Arthropods with three pairs of jointed legs – Insects

Arthropods with three pairs of jointed legs are called insects. The body of an insect is made up of three regions – head, thorax and abdomen. How many segments are there in each region? Most adults insects also have two pairs of wings.

Fig. 9.21 Butterfly

Fig. 9.22 Grasshopper

Fig. 9.23 Ant

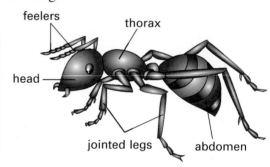

Fig. 9.24 Parts of an insect

Arthropods with four pairs of jointed legs – Arachnids

Fig. 9.25 Spider

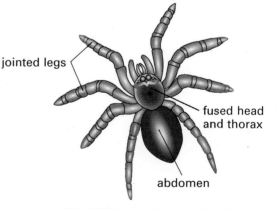

Fig. 9.26 Parts of an arachnid

The spider is classified as an arachnid, not an insect. Besides having four pairs of jointed legs, what is the one other difference between an arachnid and an insect?

Other common arachnids are shown below:

Fig. 9.27 Ticks

Fig. 9.28 Scorpion

Connect

Dust mites affect our health. Find out how dust mites can harm us at home or in school. How would you remove the dust mites?

Arthropods with more than four pairs of jointed legs

Arthropods with more than four pairs of jointed legs have many body segments which bear one or two pairs of jointed legs per segment.

Fig. 9.29 Centipede

Fig. 9.30 Millipede

Invertebrates without jointed legs

Invertebrates without jointed legs can be divided into two sub-groups according to whether they are worm-like or not worm-like as follows:

Worm-like invertebrates that are without jointed legs

Leech   Flatworm   Earthworm   Tubeworm

Fig. 9.31 Worm-like invertebrates without jointed legs

Suggest how the worm-like invertebrates shown above can be further divided into two different groups.

Other invertebrates without jointed legs (not worm-like)

Sea anemone   Snail   Starfish

Fig. 9.32 Non-worm-like invertebrates without jointed legs

Suggest how the invertebrates which are not worm-like can be further divided into two different groups.

Jellyfish

9.4 Using Keys to Identify and Classify Living Organisms

To classify living things, we look for observable characteristics that make each group or type of organisms different from the other. These differences can be used to make an identification key.

A **key** consists of clues or descriptions used in the identification of objects.

Below is an example of a key used to classify vertebrates into five different groups.

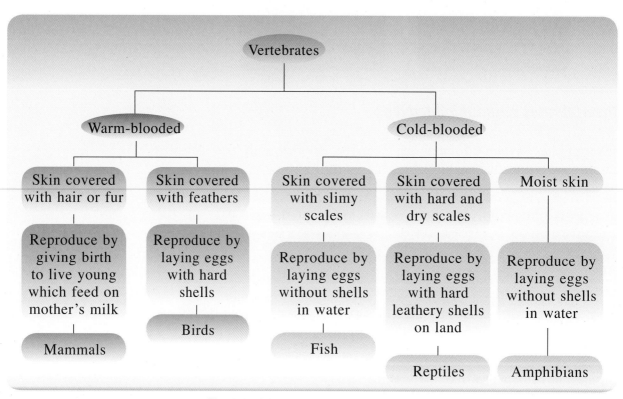

Fig. 9.33 A key to classify vertebrates

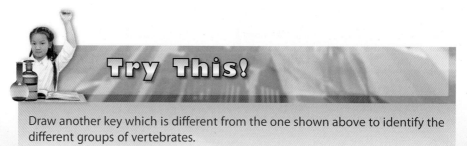

Draw another key which is different from the one shown above to identify the different groups of vertebrates.

A key is called a **dichotomous key** if objects are classified or identified by dividing them into **two smaller groups** at each step.

A dichotomous key is easy to use because users simply have to answer 'yes' or 'no' to a series of questions or select one of two contrasting descriptions.

The dichotomous key below can also be used to classify vertebrates into five different groups.

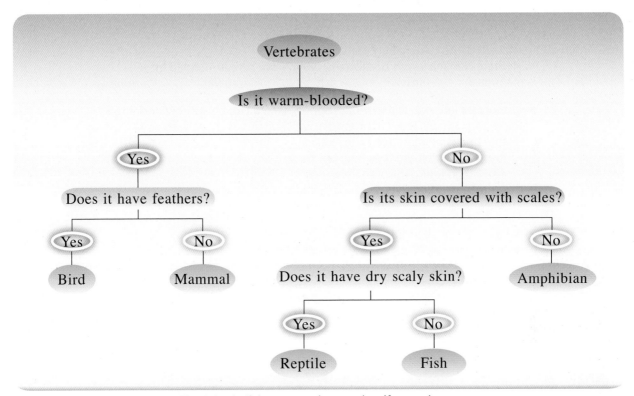

Fig. 9.34 A dichotomous key to classify vertebrates

Draw a dichotomous key to classify invertebrates into different sub-groups.

▶Activity 34 P.B.   ▶Activity 9 T.W.

Key Points

1. Living organisms are classified into major taxonomic groups and sub-groups based on common observable characteristics.
2. Classifying living organisms makes the study of living organisms easier and more systematic.
3. Plant and animal kingdoms are two major taxonomic groups.
4. Plants are classified into two main groups:
   - Flowering plants
   - Non-flowering plants, which can be sub-divided into:
     – conifers   – ferns   – mosses

5. Animals are classified into two main groups:
   - Vertebrates (animals with backbones), which can be sub-divided into:
     – mammals   – birds   – fish   – reptiles   – amphibians

   - Invertebrates (animals without backbones), which can be sub-divided into:
     – those with jointed legs (arthropods), which includes those with
       - three pairs of jointed legs (insects)
       - four pairs of jointed legs (arachnids)
       - more than four pairs of jointed legs
     – those without jointed legs, which includes those that are:
       - worm-like   - non-worm-like

6. A key consists of clues or descriptions used in the identification of objects and is often used in classifying living things.
7. A dichotomous key is a key which classifies or identifies objects by dividing them into two smaller groups at each stage.

Let's Review!

1. Why is there a need to classify living things into different major taxonomic groups and sub-groups?

2. How are living organisms classified into different major taxonomic groups?

3. Name two major taxonomic groups of plants. Differentiate between them.

4. Construct a dichotomous key to classify:

   (a) plants into flowering plants, conifers, ferns and mosses;

   (b) invertebrates into arthropods, worm-like and non-worm-like invertebrates without jointed legs.

5. Describe one observable characteristic of each of the following groups of animals:

   (a) Amphibians   (b) Birds   (c) Fish   (d) Mammals   (e) Reptiles

6. How does the classification of living things help us to understand and maintain the connections among living things?

▶Revision 9 T.W.

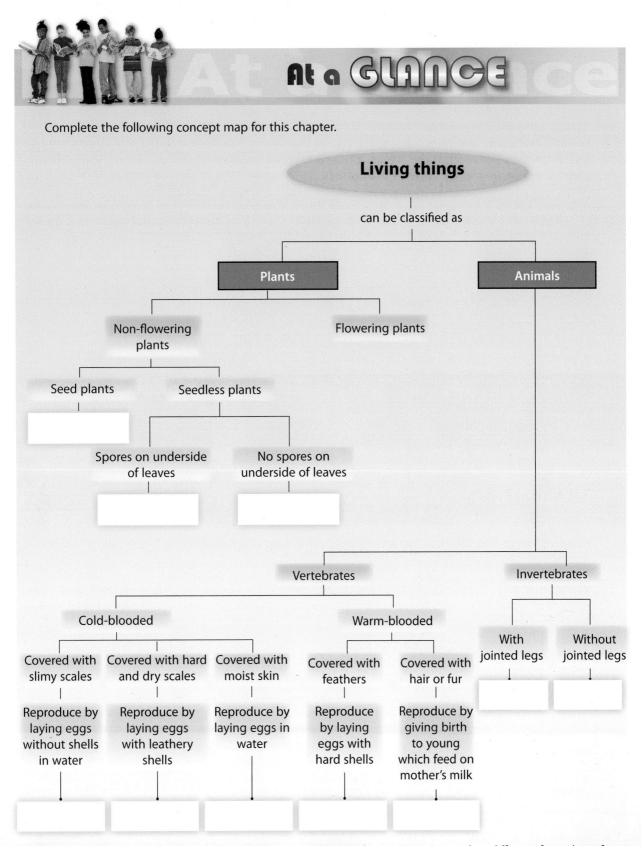

At a GLANCE

Complete the following concept map for this chapter.

Living things

can be classified as

Plants   **Animals**

Non-flowering plants   Flowering plants

Seed plants   Seedless plants

Spores on underside of leaves   No spores on underside of leaves

Vertebrates   Invertebrates

Cold-blooded   Warm-blooded   With jointed legs   Without jointed legs

Covered with slimy scales   Covered with hard and dry scales   Covered with moist skin   Covered with feathers   Covered with hair or fur

Reproduce by laying eggs without shells in water   Reproduce by laying eggs with leathery shells   Reproduce by laying eggs in water   Reproduce by laying eggs with hard shells   Reproduce by giving birth to young which feed on mother's milk

Construct a dichotomous key for plants, vertebrates and invertebrates. How is your key different from that of your classmates?

Think Tank

1. Classification enables us to observe patterns in a variety of things and makes the study of these things easier and more systematic. Things are usually classified according to some common characteristics. However, there are usually several common characteristics among living things, some of which are more important than others.

   Try classifying the living things given according to characteristics such as colours, shapes, sizes, structures, features and developments. Which classifications make more sense? Which characteristics are more important for classifying living things?

Giraffe	Man	Duck	Ostrich

2. Study the diagrams of the three animals, the crab, the jellyfish and the scorpion, which are given below.

   By comparing their common characteristics, can you say which two of these animals belong to the same group?

3. Viruses that give you a cold, chicken-pox, mumps or measles cannot reproduce on their own. They need the help of living cells to reproduce. Do you consider viruses to be living things? If so, under which kingdom would you classify them?

Models and Systems

Models of Cells and Matter
- Cells – Structure, Function and Organisation
- Particulate Model of Matter
- Simple Concepts of Atoms and Molecules

Plant and Human Systems
- Transport in Living Things
- Digestion in Animals
- Sexual Reproduction in Human Beings

• Overview •

Scientists often construct models to help in the understanding of objects or phenomena. Models are simplified representations of these objects or phenomena. Physical, conceptual and mathematical models are three different types of models used.

Processes in nature are often carried out by systems. A system consists of many parts interacting with and influencing one another. Most of the time, two or more systems can interact to perform a function too.

In this theme, we examine the atomic model and the Particulate Model of Matter. We will also study two systems in nature, the digestive system and the reproductive system.

• Key Inquiry Questions •

- What are models and systems?
- How do we evaluate whether a model used is a good representation of the real system?
- How do the physical, conceptual and mathematical models differ?
- How do the parts of a system or different systems interact to perform a function?
- Why do the different systems in our body interact with one another?

10 Cells – Structure, Function and Organisation

In this chapter, you will learn to:

- identify the different parts of an animal cell – cell surface membrane, cytoplasm, nucleus, vacuole

- identify the different parts of a plant cell – cell wall, cell surface membrane, cytoplasm, nucleus, vacuole, chloroplast

- show an understanding of the functions of the different parts of a cell, including the nucleus which contains genetic material that determines heredity

- compare a typical plant cell and a typical animal cell

- recognise that multicellular organisms include both plants and animals, cells of similar structures are organised into tissues; several tissues may make up an organ; organs are organised into systems

- explain the significance of the division of labour, even at the cellular level

- show an appreciation of the moral and social issues related to the application of genetic science

Are all the cells in an organism living and active?

A cell is the basic unit of living things. All living things are made up of one or more cells.

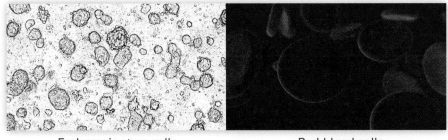

Embryonic stem cells

Red blood cells

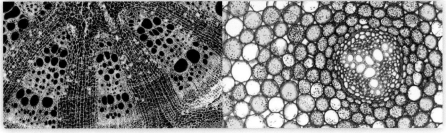

Plant stem cells

Root cells

Fig. 10.1 Different types of cells

What are the different parts of a cell? How do these parts work together to allow the cell to function? What are the similarities and differences between a typical animal cell and a typical plant cell?

10.1 Animal Cells

Fig. 10.2 represents a typical animal cell.

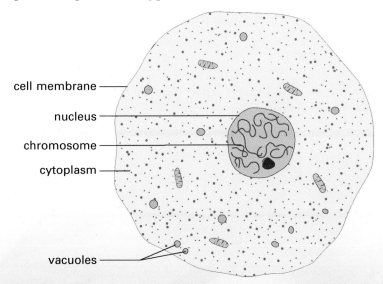

cell membrane

nucleus

chromosome

cytoplasm

vacuoles

Fig. 10.2 A typical animal cell

▶Activity 35-36 P.B.

Cell membrane

The cell membrane is a thin, partially permeable layer which controls the movement of materials into and out of the cell. Being partially permeable, it only allows certain materials to pass through it.

Cytoplasm

The cytoplasm is a jelly-like substance that contains many tiny structures such as vacuoles. Numerous chemical reactions take place in the cytoplasm where new substances are made, with energy being released or stored. The cytoplasm almost fills the cell.

Vacuoles

Vacuoles in animal cells are membrane-bound sacs containing air, liquid or food particles and are found in the cytoplasm. These vacuoles are small and numerous.

Nucleus

The nucleus controls all the activities that take place in the cell. Hence, it is also known as the 'control centre'. Chromosomes are found in the nucleus.

Chromosomes

Chromosomes are thread-like structures that contain DNA (deoxyribonucleic acid). The DNA contains information for the structure and function of the cell. Chromosomes are passed down from one generation to another. They are responsible for the inherited characteristics of an organism.

10.2 Plant Cells

Study the photograph of plant leaf cells shown in Fig. 10.3. Can you identify the different parts of a leaf cell by comparing Fig. 10.3 with Fig. 10.4?

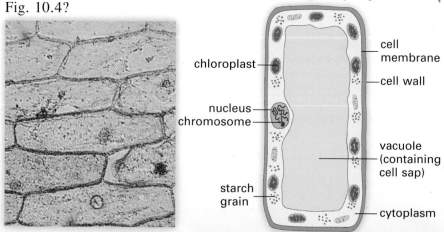

Fig. 10.3 Cells from the leaf of a plant   Fig. 10.4 A typical plant cell

▶**Activity 37 P.B.**   ▶**Activity 10 T.W.**

Cell wall

The cell wall is made up of a thick layer of cellulose. It supports a plant cell, gives it a regular shape and holds it together with other plant cells.

Cell membrane

The cell membrane is a thin partially permeable layer which controls the movement of materials into and out of the cell. Being partially permeable, it only allows certain materials to pass through it, but not others.

Vacuole

The vacuole is large and forms the biggest part of the plant cell. It usually reduces the cytoplasm to a thin lining. In every plant cell, there is usually one vacuole filled with cell sap.

Cell sap is a liquid that contains dissolved substances such as sugar and salt. It keeps the cells firm by taking in water. If the cell sap loses its water, the cells will become flaccid and the plant will wilt.

Cytoplasm

The cytoplasm is a thin lining in a plant cell. It contains the nucleus, chloroplasts and starch grains.

Chloroplasts

Chloroplasts are tiny disc-like structures containing a green pigment called chlorophyll. The chlorophyll absorbs light energy from the Sun and uses it to make food through the process of photosynthesis.

Starch grains

Stored food in the form of starch grains are commonly found in the cytoplasm.

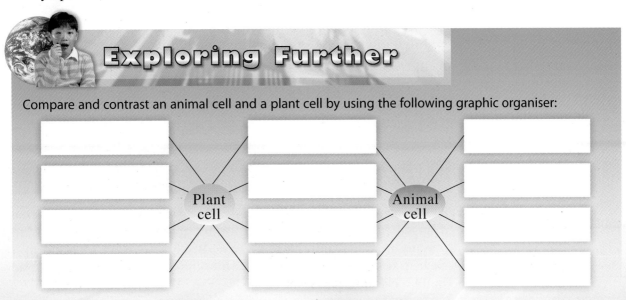

Exploring Further

Compare and contrast an animal cell and a plant cell by using the following graphic organiser:

Plant cell

Animal cell

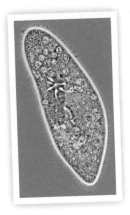

Fig. 10.5 *Paramecium*

10.3 Functions of Different Cells

A **unicellular** organism is made up of a single cell. An example is a *paramecium*, which performs all the functions to keep itself alive. Can you name the functions that are carried out by the unicellular organism?

A **multicellular** organism is made up of more than one cell. Multicellular organisms such as human beings have billions of cells. The different cells often perform different functions, but they all work together to keep the multicellular organism alive.

Different cells have different shapes and structures that are designed to perform different functions. For example, some cells are designed to:

• carry electrical impulses;   • carry oxygen around our body;

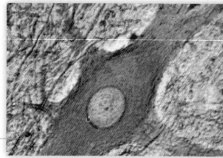

Fig. 10.6 Nerve cells   Fig. 10.7 Red blood cells

• store fats;   • control the size of openings called stomata.

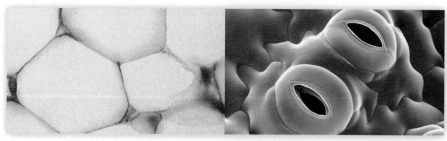

Fig. 10.8 Fat cells   Fig. 10.9 Guard cells in plants

10.4 From Cells to Tissues

Within a multicellular organism, cells of the same type are often arranged in groups or layers to form a **tissue**. Though the cells in a tissue function individually, they all work together to perform a specific task. For example, every muscle cell contracts in a muscle tissue to produce body movement.

Some animal tissues are designed to:

- contract and so allow them to move a bone/organ;
- carry electrical impulses from one part of the body to another;

Fig. 10.10 Muscle tissue

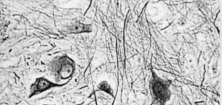

Fig. 10.11 Nerve tissue

- protect the structures beneath them;
- join all parts of the organism.

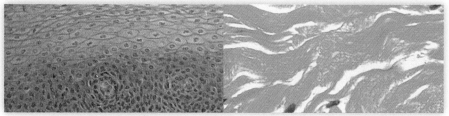

Fig. 10.12 Epithelial tissue

Fig. 10.13 Connective tissue

Some plant tissues are designed to:

- support the plant;
- carry out photosynthesis;

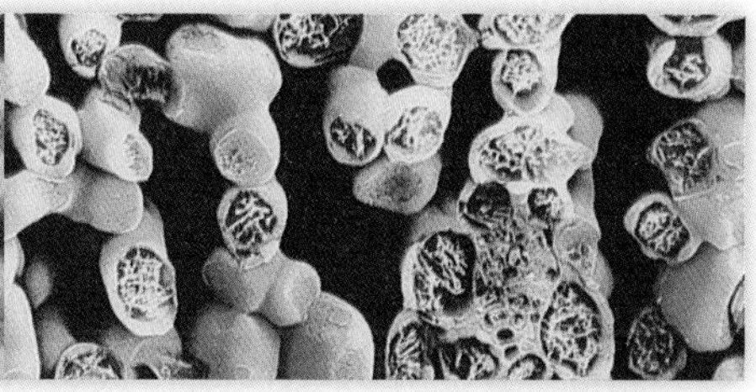

Fig. 10.14 Ground tissue

Fig. 10.15 Photosynthetic tissue

- protect a plant against injury and drying-out of its inner parts;
- transport food and water to various parts of a plant.

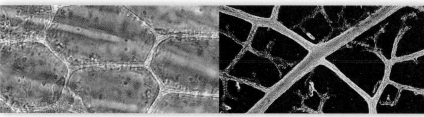

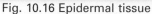

Fig. 10.16 Epidermal tissue

Fig. 10.17 Vascular tissue

How does the function of a tissue differ from the function of the cells which make up the tissue?

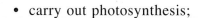

How are we similar to the cells in a tissue when caring for our country?

10.5 From Tissues to Organs

Connect

Why is it important to keep the organs in our body healthy? What should we do to keep them healthy?

Different tissues in organisms are often grouped together to form an **organ** which is responsible for carrying out more complex functions in our body. Do the different tissues in an organ perform the same function or different functions?

Some of the organs in animals are the heart, lungs, stomach, intestines, liver, kidneys, bones, skin, testes and ovaries.

Most animal organs are made up of connective tissues and some other specialised tissues. Why are connective tissues found in most animal organs?

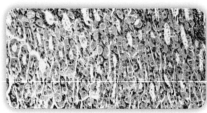

Fig. 10.18 The stomach wall consists of glandular, muscular and connective tissues.

Fig. 10.19 The heart consists of muscular, blood and connective tissues.

Describe the main function of the stomach and the heart.

An organ often performs a number of different functions. For example, our liver stores food and produces bile.

Most plants have organs such as leaves, stems, roots and flowers.

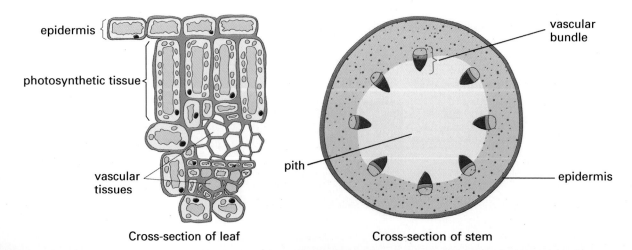

epidermis

photosynthetic tissue

vascular tissues

Cross-section of leaf

vascular bundle

pith

epidermis

Cross-section of stem

Fig. 10.20 Name the tissues found in each of the above plant organs.

Every plant organ often performs many different functions.

For example, the stem of a plant has three main functions:
1) It transports water with dissolved mineral salts from the roots to the leaves;
2) It carries food from the leaves to other parts of the plant;
3) It provides support to the plant to stand upright.

Describe the multiple functions of the roots, leaves and flowers.

1. Why does an organ have to be made up of different tissues?

2. How is the function of an organ related to the functions of its tissues?

What is the largest organ in the human body? Name its functions.

The following photographs show some of the different artificial human organs.

Artificial leg

Artificial arm

Artificial heart

The above artificial organs were jointly developed by scientists and technologists working together for years. Name the attitudes that we should adopt while working together with others. Why is it important for us to adopt these attitudes?

10.6 | From Organs to Systems

In a multicellular organism, the cells are grouped into tissues, which in turn are grouped to form organs. The organs are then linked together to form a body **system**. The functions performed by a body system are more complex than those performed by the organs.

The following diagrams show some of the body systems that are found in humans:

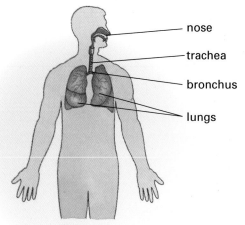

nose
trachea
bronchus
lungs

Fig. 10.21 **Respiratory system**
Takes in oxygen from the surroundings. Removes carbon dioxide and water vapour produced by respiration.

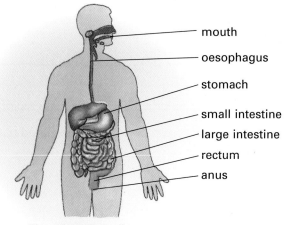

mouth
oesophagus
stomach
small intestine
large intestine
rectum
anus

Fig. 10.22 **Digestive system**
Breaks down the food we eat into simpler substances that can be absorbed by the blood.

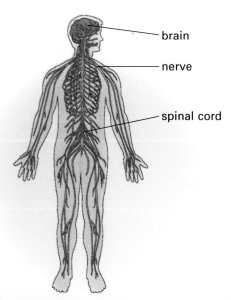

brain
nerve
spinal cord

Fig. 10.23 **Nervous system**
Controls our actions, ensures all parts of our body work smoothly together and enables us to respond to changes around us.

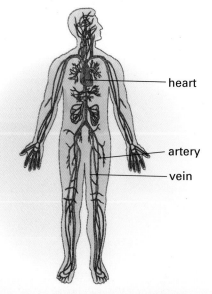

heart
artery
vein

Fig. 10.24 **Blood circulatory system**
Carries food, oxygen and water to various parts of the body. Carries wastes away to be removed.

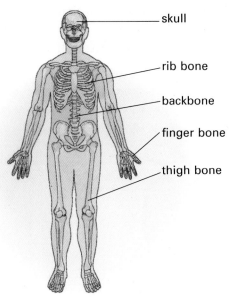

Fig. 10.25 **Skeletal system**
Supports our body, gives us shape, protects our organs and enables movement.

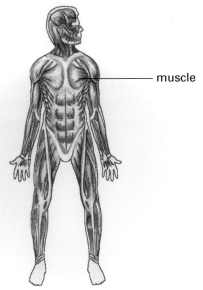

Fig. 10.26 **Muscular system**
Enables movement.

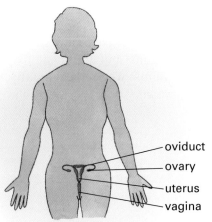

Fig. 10.27 **Female reproductive system**
Produces eggs for reproduction.

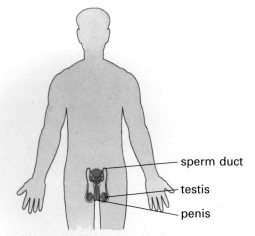

Fig. 10.28 **Male reproductive system**
Produces sperms for reproduction.

A plant has fewer systems as it is less complex than an animal. For example, the transport system found in a plant involves practically the whole plant – its roots, stem and leaves.

The transport system carries water, mineral salts and food to various parts of the plant. What will happen to the plant if its the transport system fails to function?

Can you think of any other systems found in plants?

10.7 From Systems to Organisms

Different types of multicellular organisms are made up of different numbers and types of systems. Name the systems that make up the human body.

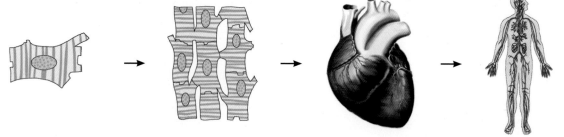

Heart muscle cell – a cell

Heart muscle – a tissue
A group of similar cells that are specialised to perform a certain function together forms a tissue.

The heart – an organ
A group of specialised tissues that are gathered in a certain part of the body to perform a particular function together forms an organ.

Circulatory system
Various organs that work together to perform a major function in the body form a system.

Fig. 10.29 An example of a cell, tissue, organ and system in a human being

In multicellular organisms, the cells are organised into tissues, the tissues into organs, the organs into systems and the systems make up the whole organism. Different systems work individually, but together, they make up the whole organism.

Exploring Further

Why is it important for multicellular organisms to be made up of different systems instead of separate individual cells?

10.8 Division of Labour

How do the functions of the single cell in a unicellular organism differ from those of the specialised cells in a multicellular organism?

In a multicellular organism, each type of cell specialises in performing one particular function. For example, the red blood cells in a human specialise in carrying oxygen around the body. The guard cells in a plant regulates gaseous exchange.

Thus, the functions of a multicellular organism as a whole are divided among its different specialised cells, each of which performs a particular function efficiently. This dividing up of the functions is called **division of labour**.

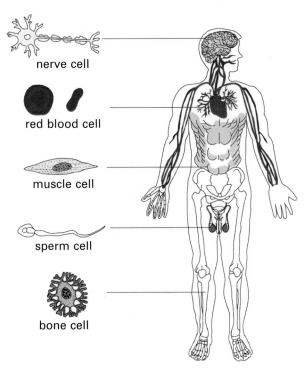

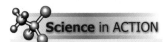

Science in ACTION

In the production lines of factories, workers specialise in doing different tasks. This leads to higher productivity and efficiency.

Fig. 10.30 Specialisation of cells leads to division of labour.

Why is there a higher degree of division of labour among the cells of a more complex and highly developed multicellular organism?

Division of labour allows different functions in a multicellular organism to be performed efficiently at the same time. For example, you can breathe and walk while your body is digesting the lunch you have just taken. What will happen to you if your body does not perform one of the functions?

▶ **Activity 38 P.B.**

Key Points

1. A cell is the basic unit of living things or organisms. All living things are made up of one or more cells.

2. The structures and functions of the different parts of a cell are shown below:

Part of cell	Structure	Functions
Cell wall	Is made up of a thick layer of cellulose around the cell membrane of a plant cell	Supports the plant cell, gives it a regular shape and holds it together with other plant cells
Cell membrane	Is a thin, partially permeable membrane around the cell	Allows only certain materials to move into or out of the cell
Cytoplasm	Is a jelly-like substance that contains many chemicals. Almost fills an animal cell; exists as a thin lining in a plant cell	Allows many chemical reactions to take place here
Vacuole	Exists as one large membrane-bound sac filled with cell sap in a plant cell; exists as numerous tiny membrane-bound sacs containing air, liquid or food, in an animal cell	Stores water, dissolved sugars and salt, making a plant cell firm or turgid by taking in water; or stores food in an animal cell
Chloroplast	Exists as a tiny disc containing chlorophyll in a plant cell	Traps sunlight to provide energy for the plant to photosynthesise
Starch grain	Exists as a tiny grain found in the cytoplasm of a plant cell	Represents the stored food that is found only in plant cells
Nucleus	Contains genetic material stored in chromosomes	Controls all activities within the cell
Chromosome	Exists as thread-like structures containing DNA	Passed down from one generation to another and determines heredity; provides DNA needed for building and controlling the cell

3. Structures of:

a typical plant cell

a typical animal cell

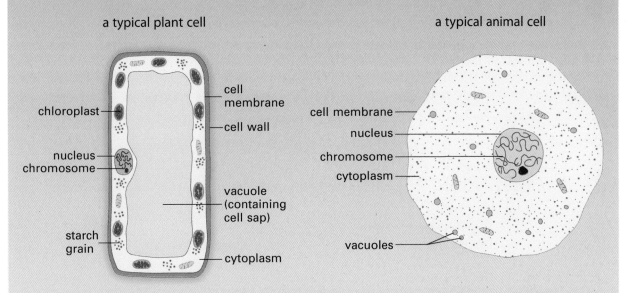

4. A unicellular organism is made up of only one cell. A multicellular organism is made up of more than one cell.

5. Different types of cells in a multicellular organism have different shapes and structures designed to perform different functions.

6. Cells of the same type are gathered in groups or layers to form tissues. Cells in a tissue work together to perform a specific task.

7. Different tissues group together to form an organ, which is responsible for carrying out more complex functions.

8. Different organs are linked together to form a system. A system carries out more complex functions than those performed by organs.

9. An organism is made up of different systems working individually as well as together.

10. The division of labour in a multicellular organism divides its functions among different specialised cells.

11. Division of labour allows different functions in a multicellular organism to be performed efficiently at the same time.

Let's Review!

1. Study the photographs shown below.

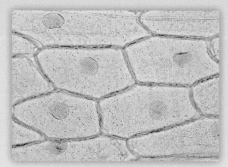

Onion cells

Human cheek cells

(a) Draw a labelled diagram to show the different parts of each cell.

(b) Describe the functions of the different parts of each cell.

2. Give three differences between plant and animal cells.

3. Which part of a cell determines the heredity of an organism's offspring?

4. Describe the organisation of cells in a human body.

5. Should our lung be classified as a tissue, an organ or a system? Explain your answer.

6. What is meant by division of labour in an organism?

7. Explain why division of labour is important for multicellular organisms even at the cellular level.

8. Explain why division of labour is not required in a unicellular organism like a bacterium.

▶ Revision 10 T.W.

At a GLANCE

Complete the following concept map for this chapter.

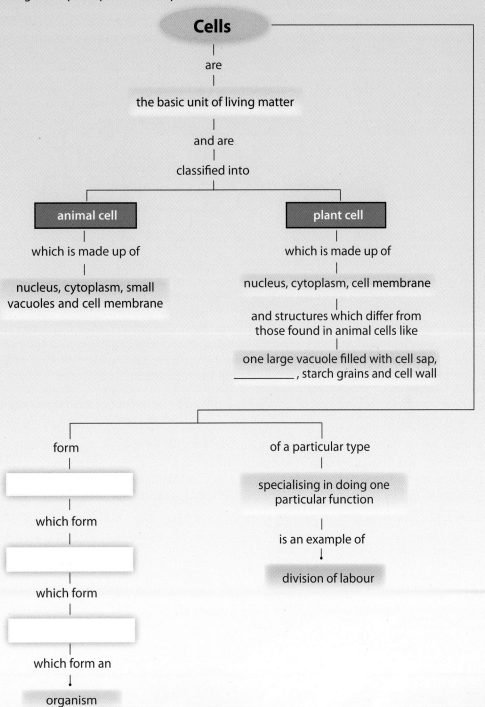

Cells

are

the basic unit of living matter

and are

classified into

animal cell

which is made up of

nucleus, cytoplasm, small vacuoles and cell membrane

plant cell

which is made up of

nucleus, cytoplasm, cell membrane

and structures which differ from those found in animal cells like

one large vacuole filled with cell sap, _____ , starch grains and cell wall

form

which form

which form

which form an

organism

of a particular type

specialising in doing one particular function

is an example of

division of labour

1. Study carefully the diagram of the cell below. Do you think it is an animal or a plant cell? Explain your answer.

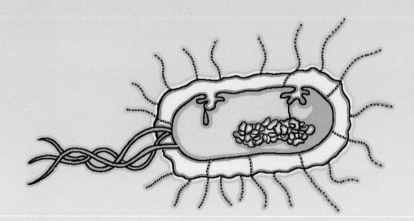

2. A gene is part of the chromosome which controls a particular characteristic of an organism. Nowadays, scientists are able to alter the genes of a plant or animal in order to change the way it grows. Some food contain substances which have had their genes altered or modified. These are called genetically modified (GM) food. GM food includes strawberries with fish genes to protect them from frost in cold weather and rice plants which have been altered to make them pest resistant. Would you buy or eat genetically modified food? Give your reasons. Would you like GM food to be labelled so that you know whether the food you bought has been modified?

3. How do you expect the cells of simple life forms to be different from our own cells in terms of quality and quantity?

4. One of the systems of a flowering plant is the transport system which transports water, dissolved mineral salts from the soil and food throughout the plant. Which system in our body performs similar functions to those of the plant transport system? What is the main difference between the food transported by the transport system in plants and those in our body?

5. Give an example from your daily life to illustrate the advantages of division of labour. Why do you think cells which perform all functions are not as common as cells which specialise in certain tasks? Suggest a disadvantage of the division of labour of cells.

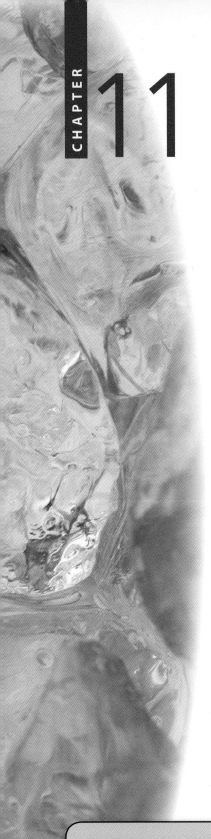

11 Particulate Model of Matter

In this chapter, you will learn to:

- show an awareness that matter is made up of small discrete particles which are in constant and random motion, using the Particulate Model of Matter

- show an understanding of the simple model of solids, liquids and gases, in terms of the arrangement and movement of the particles

- use models to understand the behaviour of molecules in the three states of matter (solid, liquid and gas)

- compare and relate the characteristics of the three states of matter in terms of the arrangement and movement of the particles

- communicate understanding of the Particulate Model of Matter in terms of the arrangement and movement of the particles

- show an appreciation of how in practice, models are constructed, justified and continuously revised as they are used to probe new phenomena and collect additional data

- show an appreciation of scientific attitudes such as creativity and open-mindedness in creating models to explain the fundamental nature of things and the willingness to re-examine existing models

- explain melting and boiling in terms of conversion of the states of matter

> The Particulate Model of Matter can be used to explain many observations. One of them is the constant temperature of melting ice. How did this model come to its present form? How does this model explain what matter is made of?

Matter makes up almost everything in the universe. Water, for example, covers about 70 % of the Earth's surface, and exists in various forms:

Glacier (solid)

Sea (liquid)

Geyser (gas)

Fig. 11.1 The three states of water

What is water, or matter in general, made up of? How does matter change from one form to another?

11.1 Particulate Model of Matter

What is matter made up of? To answer this question, we must go back nearly 2 500 years to the ancient Greeks.

The development of the Particulate Model of Matter is summarised below:

Development of the Particulate Model of Matter

Democritus	**Aristotle**	**John Dalton**	**Robert Brown**	**Albert Einstein**
(460-361 B.C.)	(460-322 B.C.)	(1766-1844)	(1773-1858)	(1879-1955)
Greek philosopher	Greek philosopher	English chemist	Scottish scientist	German-born American physicist

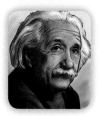

| Hypothesised that all matter is made up of tiny discrete particles called 'atoms' which are too small to be seen (discrete – discontinuous; separate). | Hypothesised that matter has a continuous composition that can be broken down into smaller and smaller pieces. | Suggested that matter is made up of small, discrete particles which are like little solid balls. | Observed with a microscope that some dead pollen grains suspended in water were constantly moving about randomly in all directions. This is known as Brownian motion (random – no fixed manner). | Explained that the dead pollen grains were moving because they were being bombarded by the moving water particles. |

Fig. 11.2 Scientists' contributions to the Particulate Model of Matter

Whose hypothesis is true – Democritus' or Aristotle's?

Based on the evidence of experiments, scientists have formulated the Particulate Model of Matter to explain what matter is really made of, and how the properties of matter may be explained.

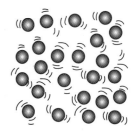

Fig. 11.3 Matter is made up of discrete particles in constant and random motion.

The Particulate Model of Matter suggests that:
- All matter is made up of small discrete particles;
- The small discrete particles in matter are in constant and random motion.

Although it is possible to explain the Particulate Model of Matter using a series of statements, it is often easier to explain it using models. A model is a way of representing something that cannot be observed directly because it is too large, too small or too complicated.

A variety of objects such as balls, marbles or even people can be used to represent the small discrete particles in matter.

11.2 Particulate Models for Solids, Liquids and Gases

Scientists use the Particulate Model of Matter to explain the differences among solids, liquids and gases in terms of the arrangement and movement of the small discrete particles in them.

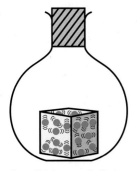

A solid has a definite shape and volume.

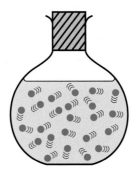

A liquid takes the shape of the part of the container it occupies, and has a definite volume.

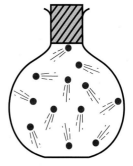

A gas always fills whatever container it is in, taking its shape and volume.

Fig. 11.4 The Particulate Model of Matter for solids, liquids and gases

How can you differentiate the three states of matter as shown in the diagrams above?

Solids

In a solid, the particles are packed closely together in a regular pattern. They are held in their fixed positions by very strong attractive forces. This arrangement of the particles explains the definite shape and volume of a solid.

Particles vibrate about their fixed positions.

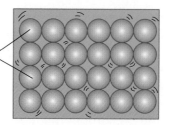

The particles in a solid only vibrate from side to side and spin about their fixed positions, but cannot move past one another.

Fig. 11.5 Model of solid

Try This!

1. A particulate model for solids is shown in the diagram.

2. What do the balls and elastic springs in the model represent?

3. Describe the motion displayed by the balls in the model when the model is shaken gently.

4. Name a type of movement of the particles in a solid that is not represented in the model.

5. Re-examine the above particulate model for solids. Suggest how the model can be further improved or replaced by a better one.

Liquids

In a liquid, the particles are also relatively close together but not as closely packed as those in a solid. The particles of a liquid are also held together by strong attractive forces like in a solid, and thus give a liquid its definite volume.

Besides vibrating sideways, the particles in a liquid can also slide randomly around one another. This explains why a liquid can flow. As the particles in a liquid do not have fixed positions, a liquid does not have a definite shape and takes the shape of the container it occupies.

Particles slide and move randomly at the same time.

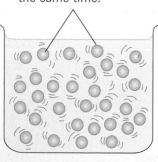

Fig. 11.6 Model of liquid

▶Activity 39–40 P.B.   ▶Activity 11.1–11.2 T.W.

Try This!

1. A particulate model for liquids is shown in the diagram.

2. What do the marbles in the model represent?

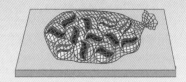

3. Describe the changes in the arrangement and movement of the marbles in the soft-net bag when the soft-net bag is transferred from one container to another of a different shape.

4. Deduce three characteristics of liquids based on the observed changes in the arrangement and movement of the marbles in the soft-net bag as described in Step 3.

5. Re-examine the above particulate model for liquids. Suggest how the particulate model for liquids can be further improved or replaced by a better one.

Gas

In a gas, the particles are widely spaced. The attractive forces holding the gas particles together are weak and can be practically ignored. So, the gas particles do not have fixed positions and can move freely and randomly in all directions at high speeds. The particles will fill up any container or space completely and quickly. This arrangement and movement of the particles in a gas explain why the shape and volume of a gas is the same as that of the container or space it fills.

Compare the shape and volume of a gas to those of a solid and liquid. Why is a gas able to flow more easily and faster than a liquid?

Particles move about freely and occupy any available space.

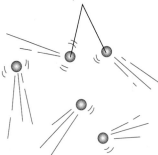

Fig. 11.7 Model of gas

Try This!

1. A particulate model for gases is shown in the diagram.

2. What do the balls in the particulate model for gases represent?

3. Describe the changes in the arrangement and movement of the balls in the transparent box when the box is shaken in all directions.

4. Deduce three characteristics of gases based on the observed changes in the arrangement and movement of the balls as described in Step 3.

5. Re-examine the particulate model for gases. Suggest how the particulate model for gases can be further improved or replaced by a better one.

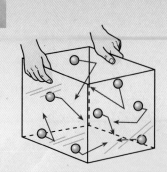

11.3 Changes in State of Matter

In the study of science, a good model is one that can be used to explain many observations. The Particulate Model of Matter has explained the shape and size of the different states of matter.

Can you use this model to explain why you can smell the perfume on a person when she enters the room?

Cooking often involves changes in the states of matter, which can also be explained by the Particulate Model of Matter.

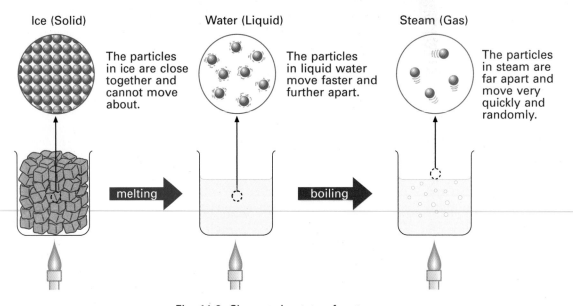

Ice (Solid)

The particles in ice are close together and cannot move about.

Water (Liquid)

The particles in liquid water move faster and further apart.

Steam (Gas)

The particles in steam are far apart and move very quickly and randomly.

melting

boiling

Fig. 11.8 Changes in state of water

The above diagram shows the changes in state of water. Name the process in which ice is converted into liquid water at a fixed temperature. Name the change of state that takes place.

Let us now examine how the Particulate Model of Matter can be used to explain the changes in states of matter during melting and boiling.

Melting

How does the temperature of ice change when you heat it? If you have a thermometer to measure the temperature, you will notice that the temperature stays constant when the ice is melting.

When solid is heated, its temperature rises until it reaches a constant temperature called the melting point. For ice, the melting point is 0 °C.

The diagram below shows the changes in the arrangement and movement of the particles in the process of melting.

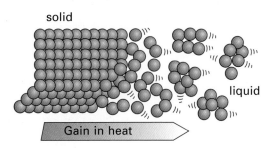

Fig. 11.9 Melting

When you are heating a solid, you are providing it with a form of energy. When melting occurs, this energy is *not* used to raise its temperature. Instead it is used to overcome (or weaken) the attractive forces that hold the solid particles together (see Fig. 11.5 on page 166). The particles are now further apart and can move randomly around one another.

Boiling

When you heat a liquid like water, its temperature will rise until it reaches the boiling point and the liquid starts to boil. The diagram below shows the changes in the arrangement and movement of the particles in the process of boiling.

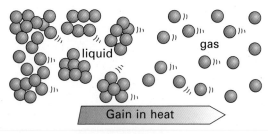

Fig. 11.10 Boiling

The particles absorb the heat energy and gain enough energy to break free from the attractive forces between particles. Do you think this energy is used to raise the temperature? How do you know?

As the amount of heat energy supplied increases, particles can move freely and randomly in all directions at high speeds like those of a gas. At that speed, they can spread to fill any container or space completely and quickly.

1. The Particulate Model of Matter suggests that:

   - All matter is made up of small discrete particles;

   - The small discrete particles in matter are in constant and random motion.

2. The Particulate Model of Matter is used to explain the properties of solids, liquids and gases in terms of the arrangement and movement of particles.

3.

	Solids	Liquids	Gases
Arrangement of particles	Particles have fixed positions and are arranged in a regular pattern. They are very closely packed.	Particles do not have fixed positions and are not so closely packed.	Particles do not have fixed positions and are far apart from one another.
Movement of particles	Particles vibrate about their fixed positions.	Particles slide and move randomly around one another.	Particles move freely and at random in all directions at high speeds and occupy any available space.
Shape and volume	Definite shape, definite volume	No definite shape, definite volume	No definite shape, no definite volume

4. Melting is a process in which a solid is converted into a liquid at a fixed temperature known as the melting point of the solid.

5. Boiling is a process in which a liquid is converted into a gas at a fixed temperature known as the boiling point of the liquid.

let's Review!

1. What is the Particulate Model of Matter?

2. Why are the particulate models of matter often being reconstructed, justified and continuously revised?

3. Use the Particulate Model of Matter to explain the following:

   (a) A solid has a definite shape and volume and it cannot flow;

   (b) A liquid has a definite volume and takes the shape of the container it fills;

   (c) A gas has no definite shape and volume. It fills any container or available space completely and quickly.

4. Explain the changes in states of matter that take place in the following processes:

   (a) Melting   (b) Boiling

▶**Revision 11 T.W.**

Complete the following concept map for this chapter.

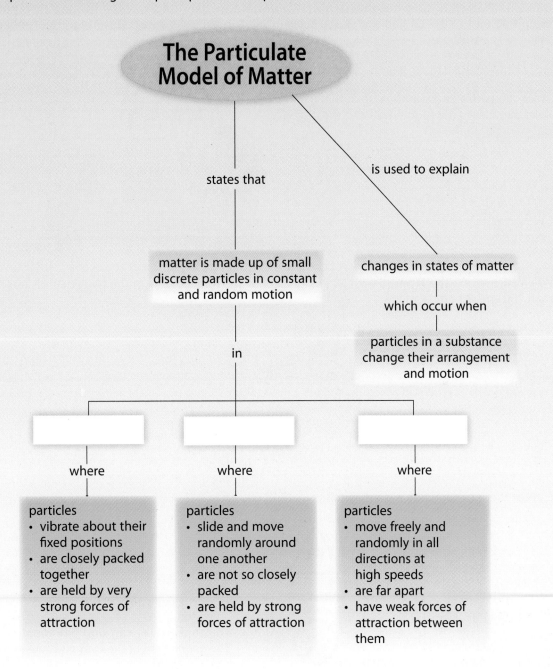

The Particulate Model of Matter

states that

is used to explain

matter is made up of small discrete particles in constant and random motion

changes in states of matter

which occur when

in

particles in a substance change their arrangement and motion

where

where

where

particles
- vibrate about their fixed positions
- are closely packed together
- are held by very strong forces of attraction

particles
- slide and move randomly around one another
- are not so closely packed
- are held by strong forces of attraction

particles
- move freely and randomly in all directions at high speeds
- are far apart
- have weak forces of attraction between them

Compare the properties of the particles in a solid, liquid and gas in a chart.

1. Carol blew up many balloons for her birthday last week. After a few days, she found that all the balloons seemed to have become smaller. Was it because the mouths of the balloons had not been tied up tightly? Or had the air particles inside the balloons escaped through the rubber walls of the balloons?

   What can you infer about the size of the solid particles in the rubber wall and the gas particles in the air?

2. When 50 cm³ of water is mixed with 50 cm³ of alcohol, the total volume of the two liquids is less than 100 cm³. Why?

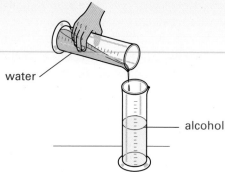

water

alcohol

3. Look at these pictures. What do they tell you about gas particles?

PETROL
HIGHLY
FLAMMABLE

NO
SMOKING

ALERT: TANKER CRASH LATEST

The tanker was carrying ammonia. The gas can affect the eyes and cause breathing problems. People living within an 8-kilometre radius of the crash were moved from their homes.

12 Simple Concepts of Atoms and Molecules

In this chapter, you will learn to:

- describe an atom as an electrically neutral entity that is made up of a positively charged nucleus (protons and neutrons) with negatively charged electrons moving round the nucleus

- show an awareness that atoms of the same element contain the same number of protons and those of different elements contain different numbers of protons

- recognise that an ion is formed when an atom gains or loses electron(s)

- show an understanding of the following:
  - molecules of an element consist of a fixed number of the same type of atoms combined together
  - molecules of a compound consist of a fixed number of different types of atoms combined together

- state the number and types of atoms, given the chemical formula of a compound

- compare atoms and molecules

- show an appreciation of scientific attitudes such as creativity and open-mindedness in creating models to explain the fundamental nature of things and the willingness to re-examine existing models

How does the smallest particle of an element look like?
How is one element different from another?

Fig. 12.1   Aluminium   Fig. 12.2   Carbon

Carbon has obviously different physical and chemical properties compared to aluminum. This is because they are different elements. What is an element made of? How is one element different from another?

12.1 What is an Atom?

Matter was believed to be made up of ...

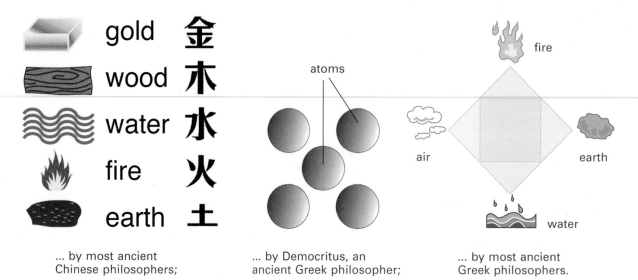

Fig. 12.3 What is matter made up of?

Democritus (460-370 B.C.) believed that if you kept on dividing matter, you would eventually obtain a single indivisible particle known as an 'atom'. Atom originates from the Greek word 'atomos' meaning 'indivisible'. What do you believe matter is made up of?

> An **atom** is defined as the smallest particle of an element that can exist.

Atoms are building blocks of all matter – living or non-living.
Are you made up of atoms?

Try This!

1. Form groups of five.

2. Each member of a group is assigned to gather information on a different model of the atom. The different models of an atom are as follows:

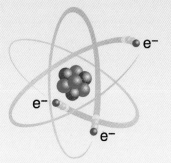

Dalton's Model 1807
The atom is a very small, hard sphere that is indivisible.

Thomson's Model 1903
The atom is a continuous mass of positive charge containing negative electrons.

Rutherford's Model 1903
The atom has a nucleus surrounded by electrons.

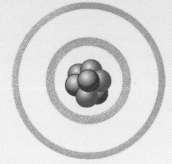

Bohr's Model 1903
The atom has a nucleus. Electrons move in fixed orbits around the nucleus.

Modern model of the atom
Electrons are found in high probability regions (blue circles) outside the nucleus. The model of the atom has changed over time as a result of new discoveries about the atom.

3. Share the information gathered with other members of your group.

4. Discuss your group's findings with the rest of the class.

5. Record the findings of your discussion in your science portfolio.

Exploring Further

Imagine you were Niels Bohr and you created the Bohr Model in 1903 to explain how an atom looks like. What kinds of attitudes have you adopted that contributed to your success?

▶**Activity 12 T.W.**

All scientists have now agreed that the atom is made up of particles called protons, neutrons and electrons. An atom basically looks like this:

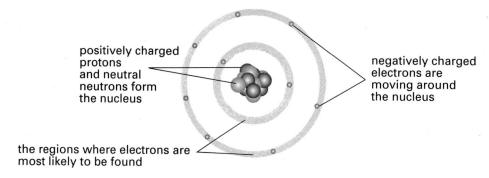

positively charged protons and neutral neutrons form the nucleus

negatively charged electrons are moving around the nucleus

the regions where electrons are most likely to be found

Fig. 12.4 Modern model of the atom

Protons are the positively charged particles concentrated at the centre of the atom. They are 'gelled' together by the **neutrons**, which are neutral and have no charge. The **nucleus** consisting of the positively charged protons and neutral neutrons is therefore positively charged.

Electrons are the mobile negatively charged particles in an atom. They move constantly at very high speeds around the nucleus, similar to the planets orbiting the Sun.

Once, scientists thought that the electrons, like the planets around the Sun, moved in fixed paths.

However, they have a different view now – that electrons move randomly all over the atom. It is impossible to pinpoint an electron's exact location in an atom. Scientists can only locate the regions where electrons are most likely to be found.

Compare the modern model of the atom with the earlier models. In what ways are these models different or similar to one another?

1. Form groups of five.

2. Each group is required to make the Dalton's model, Bohr's model, Thomson's model, Rutherford's model and the modern model of the atom. You may use straws and ping pong balls, or toothpicks and plasticine.

3. Present your group's model to the class.

4. Obtain peer evaluation on your group's models from the class.

12.2 Atoms of Elements

Study the diagram below that represents a helium atom.

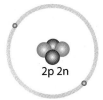 2p 2n

In an electrically neutral atom,
number of protons = number of electrons

Fig. 12.5 A helium atom

The helium atom has two protons and two electrons. Because the charges on the protons and electrons balance one another, the helium atom is electrically neutral.

The Periodic Table of Elements on page 80 can show you the number of protons and neutrons in the nucleus of an atom. Try locating the element nitrogen (N) in the Periodic Table. It is represented by:

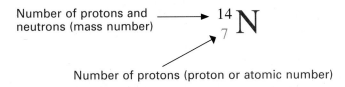

Number of protons and neutrons (mass number) ⟶ $^{14}_{7}N$

Number of protons (proton or atomic number)

The atoms of different elements contain different numbers of protons.

The number of neutrons and protons are the same in a nitrogen nucleus. Is this true for the atoms of all elements? Can you find evidence to support your answer?

Science NUGGET

Atoms are so small that it is difficult to imagine how small they really are. For example, ten million (10 000 000) atoms of magnesium placed side by side would fit across a pin head!

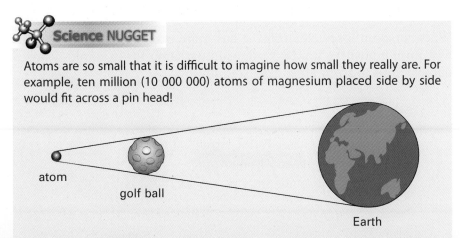

atom

golf ball

Earth

An atom is smaller than a golf ball by the same proportion as the golf ball is smaller than the Earth.

Representing Atoms

Circles are commonly used to represent atoms.

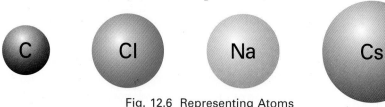

Note: Different coloured circles are used here to represent different atoms, but real atoms are not coloured.

Fig. 12.6 Representing Atoms

Why are circles of different sizes used to represent the atoms of different elements?

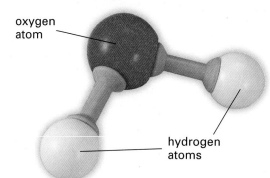

oxygen atom

hydrogen atoms

There are also other ways to represent atoms in a substance. The model in Fig. 12.7 uses spheres to show the arrangement of oxygen and hydrogen atoms in water.

Fig. 12.7 A molecular model of water

12.3 How Are Ions Formed?

When chemical changes occur in an element, its atoms may gain or lose electrons to form charged particles called **ions**.

The following diagrams show the formation of ions. Study them carefully.

When an atom loses electrons, it has more protons than electrons. It will form a positive ion. Take the sodium atom for example. It loses one electron to form a positive sodium ion:

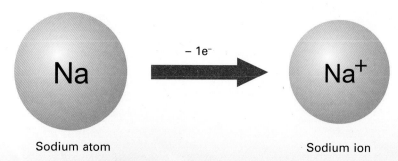

$-1e^-$

Na

Na$^+$

Sodium atom

Sodium ion

Fig. 12.8 Formation of a sodium ion

The ion formed has a symbol Na$^+$.

If an atom gains electrons, it will form a negative ion. Take the chlorine atom as an example. It gains one electron to form a negative chloride ion.

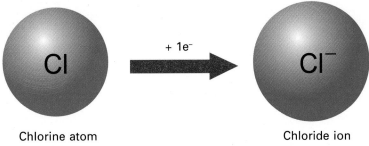

Chlorine atom   Chloride ion

Fig. 12.9 Formation of a chloride ion

Compared to a chlorine atom, how many more electrons than protons are there in a chloride ion Cl^-? How do you represent an atom of magnesium (Mg) which has lost two electrons?

Can an atom become an ion by gaining or losing a proton? Why?

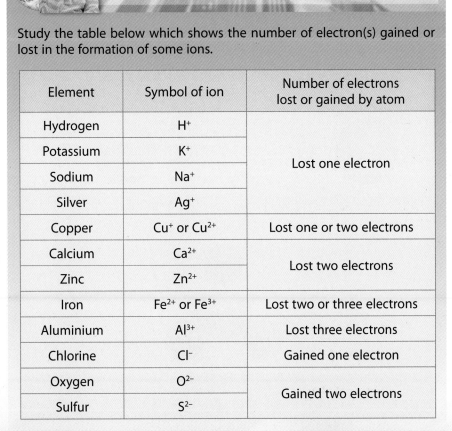

Exploring Further

Study the table below which shows the number of electron(s) gained or lost in the formation of some ions.

Element	Symbol of ion	Number of electrons lost or gained by atom
Hydrogen	H^+	Lost one electron
Potassium	K^+	
Sodium	Na^+	
Silver	Ag^+	
Copper	Cu^+ or Cu^{2+}	Lost one or two electrons
Calcium	Ca^{2+}	Lost two electrons
Zinc	Zn^{2+}	
Iron	Fe^{2+} or Fe^{3+}	Lost two or three electrons
Aluminium	Al^{3+}	Lost three electrons
Chlorine	Cl^-	Gained one electron
Oxygen	O^{2-}	Gained two electrons
Sulfur	S^{2-}	

Are positive ions usually formed from metals or non-metals? What about negative ions?

▶Activity 43 P.B.

12.4 What is a Molecule?

> A **molecule** is made up of two or more atoms of the same type or different types that are combined together. Molecules exist in both elements and compounds.

Molecules of elements consist of a fixed number of the same type of atoms combined together. For example, a chlorine molecule consists of two chlorine atoms combined together.

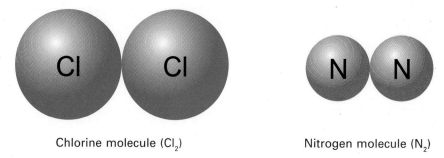

Chlorine molecule (Cl_2) Nitrogen molecule (N_2)

Fig. 12.10 Molecules of elements are made up of the same types of atoms.

Molecules of compounds consist of a fixed number of different types of atoms combined together. For example, a carbon monoxide molecule consists of a carbon atom and an oxygen atom combined together.

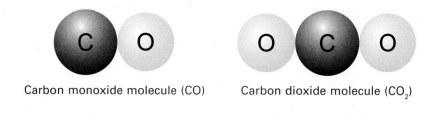

Carbon monoxide molecule (CO) Carbon dioxide molecule (CO_2)

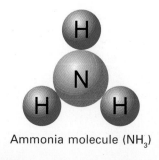

Ammonia molecule (NH_3)

Fig. 12.11 Molecules of compounds are made up of different types of atoms.

▶Activity 41–42 P.B.

12.5 Chemical Formula

The chemical formula of a compound states the number and types of atoms in each molecule of a compound.

For example, nitrogen dioxide is represented by:

the chemical symbol of nitrogen ———— NO_2

the chemical symbol of oxygen

the number shows two oxygen atoms in the compound

There are two ways to describe the number and types of atoms in a molecule of a compound.

Take water as an example.

1. Using words: or   2. Using a chemical formula:

   'Each molecule of
   water contains two
   atoms of hydrogen and H_2O
   one atom of oxygen
   combined together.'

What are the advantages and disadvantages of using the chemical formula of a compound?

Exploring Further

A glucose molecule consists of six carbon atoms, twelve hydrogen atoms and six oxygen atoms combined together. Write down the chemical formula for glucose. Is the glucose molecule an example of a molecule of an element or a compound? Explain your answer.

Key Points

1. Scientific attitudes such as creativity and open-mindedness are adopted by scientists to create models to explain the fundamental nature of things.

2. An atom is defined as the smallest particle of an element that can exist.

3. Protons are positively charged particles concentrated at the centre of the atom.

4. Protons are 'gelled' together by the neutrons, which are neutral and have no charge.

5. The nucleus consists of positively charged protons and neutral neutrons and is therefore positively charged.

6. Electrons are negatively charged particles. They move constantly at very high speeds around the nucleus.

7. In an electrically neutral atom, the number of protons is equal to the number of electrons.

8. Atoms of different elements contain different numbers of protons.

9. Circles of different sizes are often used to represent atoms of different elements.

10. When chemical changes occur in an element, its atoms may gain or lose electrons to form charged particles called ions.

11. When an atom loses electron(s), it forms a positive ion. When an atom gains electron(s), it forms a negative ion.

12. A molecule is made up of two or more atoms of the same type or different types that are combined together.

13. Molecules of elements consist of a fixed number of the same type of atoms combined together.

14. Molecules of compounds consist of a fixed number of different types of atoms combined together.

let's Review!

1. Which part of an atom is (a) positively charged; (b) negatively charged?

2. (a) Name two scientific attitudes that are often used in creating models of atoms.

   (b) How do the scientific attitudes named in (a) help in creating models to explain the fundamental nature of things?

3. What makes an atom an electrically neutral entity?

4. State the difference between atoms of the same element and atoms of different elements.

5. How is an ion formed?

6. Describe the relationship between the number of protons and electrons in:

   (a) a positive ion;

   (b) a negative ion;

   (c) an atom.

7. (a) State a similarity and a difference between the molecules of an element and the molecules of a compound.

   (b) Give an example of a molecule of:

      (i) an element;

      (ii) a compound.

8.   NO   HCl SO_2 NH_4OH $C_6H_{12}O_6$

   (a) Name the number and types of atoms in each of the above chemical formulae.

   (b) Why are there at least two chemical symbols in the chemical formulae of the above compounds?

9. What are the benefits of using the chemical formulae of compounds when communicating scientific information?

10. (a) Distinguish between an atom and a molecule of the same element.

   (b)

   | Hydrogen atom (H) | Oxygen atom (O) | Hydrogen molecule (H_2) | Oxygen molecule (O_2) | Ozone molecule (O_3) | Water molecule (H_2O) |

      (i) Which of the above is a molecule of an element?

      (ii) Which of the above is a molecule of a compound?

▶ **Revision 12 T.W.**

Complete the following concept map for this chapter.

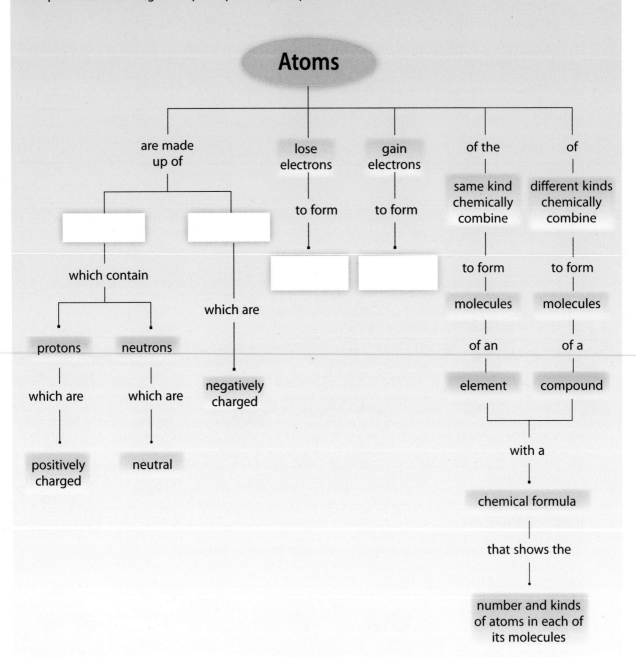

Atoms

- are made up of
  - [ ]
    - which contain
      - protons
        - which are
          - positively charged
      - neutrons
        - which are
          - neutral
  - [ ]
    - which are
      - negatively charged
- lose electrons
  - to form
    - [ ]
- gain electrons
  - to form
    - [ ]
- of the same kind chemically combine
  - to form
    - molecules
      - of an
        - element
- of different kinds chemically combine
  - to form
    - molecules
      - of a
        - compound

element / compound
- with a
  - chemical formula
    - that shows the
      - number and kinds of atoms in each of its molecules

Construct a chart to compare atoms of the elements hydrogen and sodium. What are their similarities and differences?

Think Tank

1. (a) Why is the Rutherford model of the atom often taught in schools when the modern model of the atom gives a more accurate picture of the structure of the atom?

   (b) Nuclear scientists have discovered the existence of over 100 subatomic particles, some of which are believed to be the building blocks of protons, neutrons and electrons. Is it possible for the modern model of the atom to be changed in future?

2. Opposite charges attract each other. Like charges repel each other. What problems do you think this causes inside an atom and an ion?

3. A scientist conducted an experiment in which high energy, positively charged particles called alpha particles, were directed at a very thin piece of gold foil. He found that most of the alpha particles passed right through the gold foil, but some of them were deflected back in the direction of the source. Bearing in mind that like charges repel each other, suggest which of the models – Dalton's, Thomson's or Rutherford's – was based on this experiment. Explain your choice.

Dalton's Model 1807

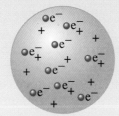

Thomson's Model 1903

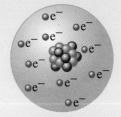

Rutherford's Model 1903

4. What do you think will happen to water molecules when:

   (a) water boils;

   (b) electricity is passed through water during electrolysis?

13 Transport in Living Things

In this chapter, you will learn to:

- explain the need for a transport system in human beings and plants

- infer that diffusion is the net movement of molecules from a region of higher concentration to a region of lower concentration

- infer that osmosis involves the movement of water molecules when two solutions of unequal concentration are separated by a partially permeable membrane

- describe briefly the process of absorption of water and mineral salts by the roots of a plant

- describe briefly the transport of water and manufactured food substances in the plant

- describe briefly how blood acts as a transport medium

- explain how diffusion and osmosis are involved in the transport system

- show an appreciation of scientific attitudes such as curiosity, objectivity and accuracy in investigations of diffusion and osmosis

How is the blood circulatory system in a human being similar to a road transport system?

The food that you have just eaten and the oxygen that you have just breathed in - how are they transported to every cell in your body?

Look at the back of your hand. You would see a pattern of veins. What role do the veins, or the blood flowing inside the veins, play in the transportation of substances in and out of our cells?

Fig. 13.1 Veins on the back of a hand

Look at the veins on a leaf. The pattern looks similar to the blood veins at the back of your hands. Does a plant have a similar system for transporting substances too?

Fig. 13.2 Veins on a leaf

13.1 Transport of Substances Into and Out of Cells

Every cell in a living thing has to continually exchange substances with its surroundings to stay alive, grow and do work. For example, our body cells take in digested food and oxygen which provide them with energy to do work, grow and stay alive. In addition, waste products such as carbon dioxide and urea (found in urine) must also be removed from the cells.

All substances that enter or leave a cell will have to pass through its partially permeable cell membrane. A **partially permeable membrane** is a membrane that has such small pores that it allows some molecules to pass through but not others.

How do substances enter or leave a cell? Why is it important for substances to enter or leave the cells rapidly?

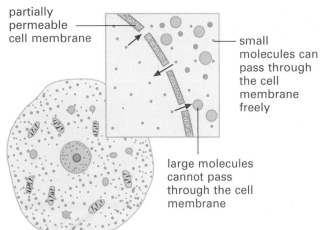

partially permeable cell membrane

small molecules can pass through the cell membrane freely

large molecules cannot pass through the cell membrane

Fig. 13.3 A close-up view of the partially permeable cell membrane of an animal cell

Try This!

Name the substance that plants normally take in from their surroundings during the day but give out at night.

13.2 Diffusion and Osmosis

The substances move in and out of a cell or organism mainly by two methods: diffusion and osmosis.

Diffusion

Diffusion is the net movement of molecules from a region of higher concentration to a region of lower concentration. It occurs when there is a difference in concentration. The greater the difference in concentration, the faster the rate of diffusion.

Diffusion can be observed in our everyday activities.

Fig. 13.4 Food cooked in the kitchen can be smelled from other rooms in the house. The molecules (gaseous) that give the smell move from the food to the other parts of the house by diffusion.

Fig. 13.5 Sugar dissolves in a cup of tea without being stirred. The sugar will soon spread to the whole cup even if you do not stir it.

Can you use the Particulate Model of Matter (Chapter 11) to explain how diffusion takes place? Why would the diffusion of a gas be faster than the diffusion of a liquid?

▶Activity 44–45 P.B.

Osmosis

Examine the following experiment:

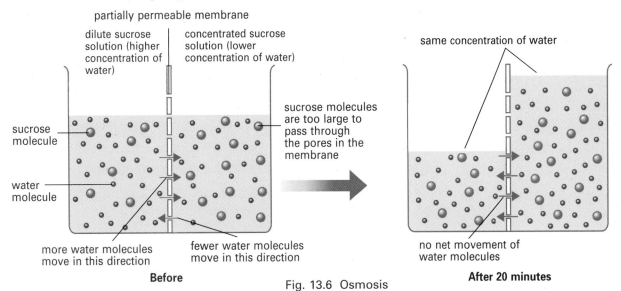

Before

After 20 minutes

Fig. 13.6 Osmosis

Can you describe the movement of the water molecules in the above experiment?

> **Osmosis** is the net movement of water molecules through a partially permeable membrane, from a region where there is a higher concentration of water molecules to a region where there is a lower concentration of water molecules.

Osmosis will stop when the concentration of the solute is the same on both sides of the partially permeable membrane.

The following diagrams illustrate how animal cells like red blood cells react when they are placed in sucrose solutions of different concentrations.

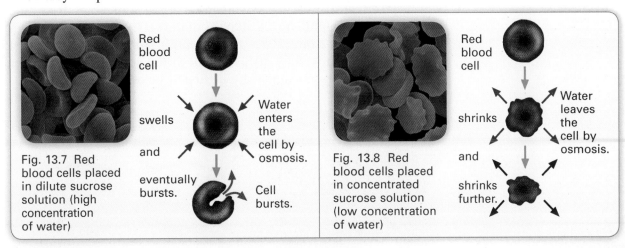

Fig. 13.7 Red blood cells placed in dilute sucrose solution (high concentration of water)

Red blood cell

swells and eventually bursts.

Water enters the cell by osmosis.

Cell bursts.

Fig. 13.8 Red blood cells placed in concentrated sucrose solution (low concentration of water)

Red blood cell

shrinks and shrinks further.

Water leaves the cell by osmosis.

Can you explain how osmosis causes the red blood cells to shrink or swell when immersed in sucrose solutions of different concentrations?

▶ **Activity 46 P.B.**

The pictures below show what happens when a plant cell is placed in a solution with a higher concentration of water:

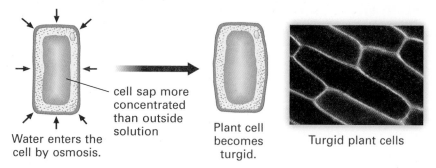

cell sap more concentrated than outside solution

Water enters the cell by osmosis.

Plant cell becomes turgid.

Turgid plant cells

Fig. 13.9 Plant cell placed in solution with higher concentration of water

The pictures below show what happens when a plant cell is placed in a solution with a lower concentration of water:

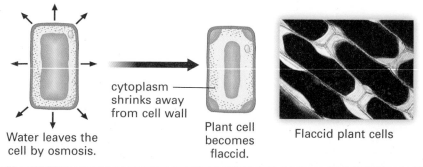

cytoplasm shrinks away from cell wall

Water leaves the cell by osmosis.

Plant cell becomes flaccid.

Flaccid plant cells

Fig. 13.10 Plant cell placed in solution with lower concentration of water

13.3 Transport System in Unicellular Organisms

In a unicellular (one-cell) organism, oxygen and food from the surroundings can rapidly reach all parts of the cell by diffusing through its cell membrane. Similarly, waste products from the organism can also be rapidly removed by diffusing out of the cell. How does water enter or leave the organism — by diffusion or osmosis?

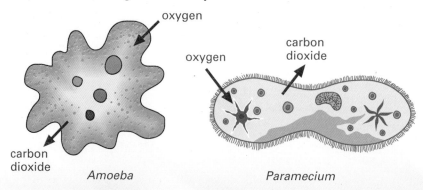

oxygen

carbon dioxide

oxygen

carbon dioxide

Amoeba

Paramecium

Fig. 13.11 Some unicellular organisms

13.4 Transport System in Plants

The following diagram shows the transport system in a plant.

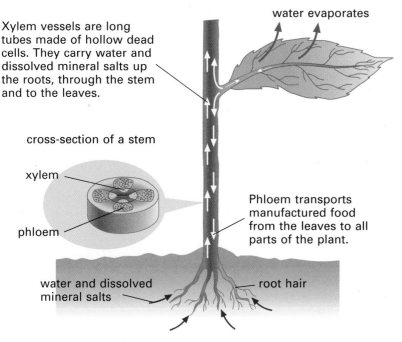

Xylem vessels are long tubes made of hollow dead cells. They carry water and dissolved mineral salts up the roots, through the stem and to the leaves.

water evaporates

cross-section of a stem

xylem

phloem

Phloem transports manufactured food from the leaves to all parts of the plant.

water and dissolved mineral salts

root hair

Fig. 13.12 Transport system in plants

The root hairs use osmosis to absorb water from the soil. When the concentration of water is lower in the root hairs than the soil, water from the soil will move through the partially permeable membrane into the root hair cells.

Water moves up a plant via the xylem vessels. Two forces, namely transpirational pull and root pressure, are responsible for moving water up the xylem vessels. Manufactured food is transported within the phloem.

When the concentration of dissolved mineral salts in the soil is lower than that in the root hairs, the mineral salts are absorbed into the cells of the root hairs by active transport. Active transport in the root hairs uses energy that is released when the plant respires.

▶Activity 47 P.B.   ▶Activity 13 T.W.

13.5 Transport System in Human Beings

The transport system found in Man is the blood circulatory system. It consists of a heart, blood vessels and blood. It carries digested food, oxygen and other useful substances to all parts of our body. It also carries carbon dioxide and other waste products from all parts of our body to certain organs where they are removed.

Blood is made up of **red blood cells**, **white blood cells** and **platelets** suspended in a yellowish liquid called **plasma**. It functions as a transport medium carrying various substances from one part of the body to another. The table below shows the substances transported by the different components of blood.

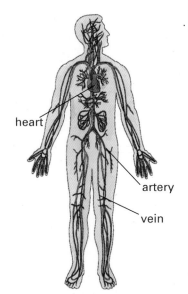

Fig. 13.13 Blood circulatory system in Man

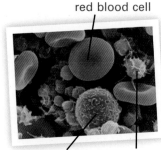

Fig. 13.14 Microscopic structure of blood

Substance(s)	Transported by	Transported from	Transported to
Dissolved food substances	Plasma	Small intestine	All parts of the body
Water	Plasma	Small and large intestine	All parts of the body
Oxygen	Red blood cells	Lungs	All parts of the body
Carbon dioxide	Plasma	All parts of the body	Lungs
Urea	Plasma	Liver	Kidneys
Hormones	Plasma	Glands	All parts of the body
Heat	Plasma	Liver and muscles	All parts of the body

Table 13.1 Substances transported by the diffferent components of blood

Exploring Further

1. Why are red blood cells classified as a specialised transport medium?

2. How would a reduced number of red blood cells affect a person's health?

3. Name two substances carried by blood that provide energy to cells.

Red blood cells

The minute spaces between tissue cells contain a colourless liquid called the **tissue fluid**. The tissue fluid carries dissolved food substances, oxygen and other waste products between the blood and the body cells.

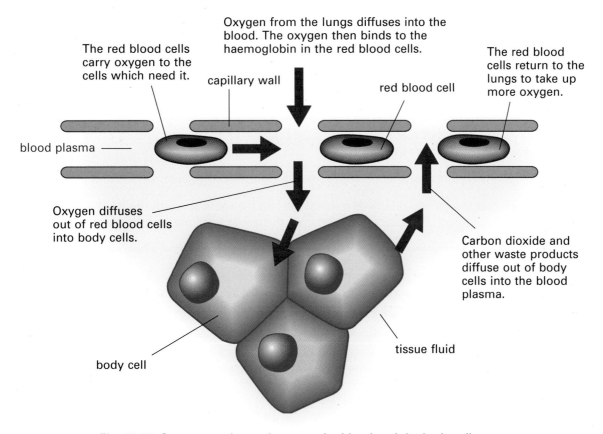

The red blood cells carry oxygen to the cells which need it.

capillary wall

Oxygen from the lungs diffuses into the blood. The oxygen then binds to the haemoglobin in the red blood cells.

red blood cell

The red blood cells return to the lungs to take up more oxygen.

blood plasma

Oxygen diffuses out of red blood cells into body cells.

Carbon dioxide and other waste products diffuse out of body cells into the blood plasma.

tissue fluid

body cell

Fig. 13.15 Gaseous exchange between the blood and the body cells

The dissolved food substances and oxygen diffuse from the blood into the tissue fluid and then into the cells. Carbon dioxide and other waste products diffuse from the cells into the tissue fluid and then into the blood, which carries the waste products away for removal.

Try This!

What happens to an organ in our body if blood supply to it is cut off? Explain your answer.

Science NUGGET

A red blood cell has a lifespan of about four months. During this time, it would have made about 172 000 journeys around the body!

Key Points

1. Every cell in a living thing has to continually exchange substances with its surroundings to stay alive, grow and do work.

2. Diffusion is the net movement of molecules from a region of higher concentration to a region of lower concentration.

3. Osmosis is the net movement of water molecules through a partially permeable membrane, from a region of higher concentration of water molecules to a region of lower concentration of water molecules.

4. Water enters a plant through its root hairs by osmosis. Dissolved mineral salts enter a plant through its root hairs by diffusion or active transport.

5. The transport system in plants consists of two types of tubes called the xylem vessels and phloem.

6. The xylem vessels carry water and dissolved mineral salts up the roots, through the stem and to the leaves. The phloem transports manufactured food from the leaves to all parts of the plant.

7. The transport system in Man is the blood circulatory system, which consists of a heart, blood vessels and blood.

8. The blood carries digested food, oxygen and other useful substances to all parts of the body. It also carries carbon dioxide and other waste products from all parts of our body to certain organs where they are removed.

9. The minute spaces between tissue cells contain a colourless liquid called the tissue fluid. It carries dissolved food substances, oxygen and other waste products between the blood and body cells.

Let's Review!

1. Only certain substances can enter or leave the cells. Why?

2. How is osmosis similar to or different from diffusion?

3. Why is there a need for a transport system in human beings and plants?

4. Describe briefly how water and mineral salts are

   (a) absorbed into a plant through its roots;

   (b) transported from the roots, up the stem and to the leaves.

5. How are the manufactured food substances in the leaves of a plant transported to the other parts of the plant?

6. Describe briefly how blood acts as a transport medium to carry substances around our body.

▶Revision 13 T.W.

At a GLANCE

Complete the following concept map for this chapter.

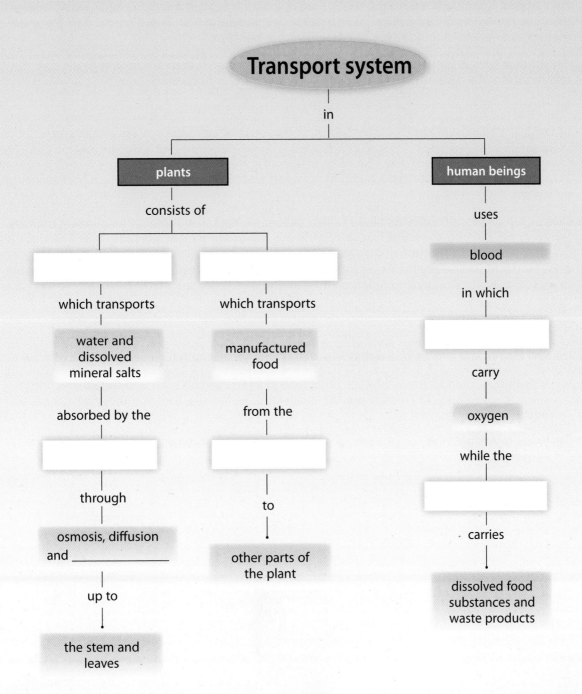

Transport system

in

| plants | human beings |

consists of — uses

blood

in which

which transports — which transports

water and dissolved mineral salts — manufactured food — carry

absorbed by the — from the — oxygen

while the

through — to

osmosis, diffusion and _____ — other parts of the plant — carries

up to

the stem and leaves — dissolved food substances and waste products

1. You are given a bottle of perfume. Design an experiment to find out how fast the smell of the perfume spreads across a room. You will need to consider how you will decide when the smell of the perfume has reached a particular part of the room. Would you always get the same results? Would you get the same results in a different room? How about in the same room but on a different day? Try to take these problems into account when you design your experiment.

2. The *Amoeba* lives in fresh water. It has a small contractile vacuole which fills up with water, and then empties this water outside the cell. It does this continuously at frequent intervals.

   (a) Explain why the freshwater amoeba needs a contractile vacuole to keep itself alive.

   (b) Explain why the kind of amoeba that lives in the sea does not need to have a contractile vacuole in its cell.

3. Suggest why plants do not need a pump to transport materials unlike animals which have hearts to do the job.

4. Dialysis is a process of removing blood from a patient whose kidneys are not functioning properly, purifying the blood using a machine and returning it into the patient's bloodstream. The dialysis machine replaces the function of the kidneys by removing waste substances from the blood. This is done by diffusion whereby the blood is brought into contact with one side of a partially permeable membrane which has a sterile solution on the other side.

   (a) How do you think the waste substances in the blood such as urea are removed from the blood?

   (b) Will the red and white blood cells and platelets which make up the blood be removed? Why?

   (c) Diffusible substances needed by the body such as sugars, amino acids and certain amounts of salts can go through the membrane. What can be done to make sure that these substances are not removed by dialysis?

   (d) Water from the blood can also diffuse through the membrane. Why is it not removed by dialysis?

▶ Portfolio Assessment 13 T.W.

14 Digestion in Animals

In this chapter, you will learn to:

- explain why most food must be digested

- infer that the end products of digestion are used for cellular processes like respiration, growth and tissue repair

- explain what is meant by digestion

- describe how a digestive system helps in digestion of food and the part played by enzymes in digestion (Only classes of enzymes such as amylase, protease and lipase are needed. Specific names of enzymes are not required.)

- identify the main parts of a digestive system and the processes that take place

- show an appreciation of scientific attitudes such as curiosity, objectivity and accuracy in investigations on the digestive system

What happens to the food we eat when it enters our body?

Food is our source of energy.

But we need to break the food down into small (really small) bits so that our cells can use them.

In the coming sections, we will examine how our body does that with a system of organs.

Fig. 14.1 Food as a source of energy

14.1 Why Must Most Food be Broken Down?

When a patient cannot eat, simple sugar (glucose) solution is usually injected directly into her bloodstream.

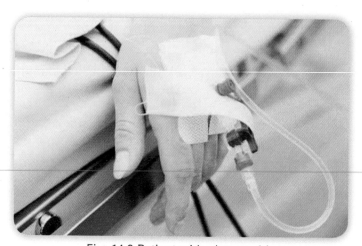

Fig. 14.2 Patient with glucose drip

This solution can be absorbed directly by her cells to release energy for bodily functions like respiration.

The cells in our body also need other nutrients for growth and tissue repair. So can we just inject food into our blood?

The problem is that our intestinal walls only allow small, simple food molecules to pass through. Only then can they be absorbed by the blood and be transported to all parts of our body.

The food we eat consists of large, complex molecules like starch, proteins and fats. They have to be broken down into smaller, simpler ones before passing through the intestinal walls.

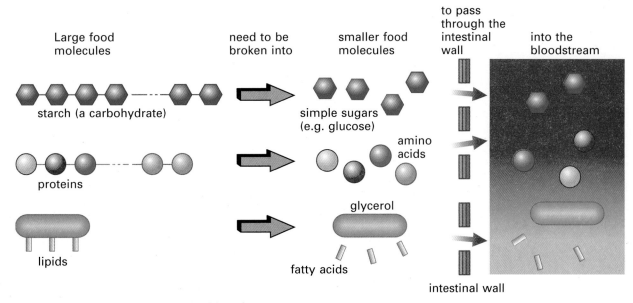

Fig. 14.3 Digestion processes

> The process of breaking down complex food molecules into smaller, simpler ones is called **digestion**.

Besides simple sugars, vitamins, mineral salts and water can also be absorbed into our bloodstream directly.

14.2 Digestion

The two main processes of digestion are physical and chemical digestion.

Physical Digestion

Fig. 14.4 Chewing brings about physical digestion in the mouth.

> **Physical or mechanical digestion** is the breaking down of food into smaller pieces. It increases the surface area of food but does not change the chemical structure of the food.

Physical digestion is brought about by the
- chewing action in the mouth;
- churning and squeezing action by the stomach; and
- action of bile salts on fats in the small intestines

Try This!

1. Add 10 drops of bile salt solution to 1 cm³ of peanut oil in a test tube.

2. Observe the mixture of bile salt solution and peanut oil.

3. Stopper the test tube and shake it for 30 seconds.

4. Observe the mixture and record any physical changes in your science portfolio.

This activity simulates an action in the mechanical digestion of lipids. What is this action called?

The physical digestion of the food is not enough to reduce them into simpler molecules. The molecules are just smaller but still as complex. How can the food molecules be further reduced in size?

Chemical Digestion

Fig. 14.5 Bread

Chew a small piece of bread in your mouth. How does it taste?

If you keep the chewed piece of bread in your mouth for a few more minutes, you will find that it will taste sweet.

You have just started digesting the bread – in your mouth!

Your mouth does not just digest the bread physically (by chewing). It has also digested it chemically – with the help of your saliva!

> **Chemical digestion** is the breaking down of large, complex food molecules into smaller, simpler food molecules.

It happens when a chemical reaction is used to break down the complex food molecules into simpler ones.

Like all other chemical reactions in our body, chemical digestion also involves enzymes. **Enzymes** are special types of proteins produced by our body cells that can speed up specific chemical reactions in our body.

Study Fig. 14.6 to understand how enzymes work.

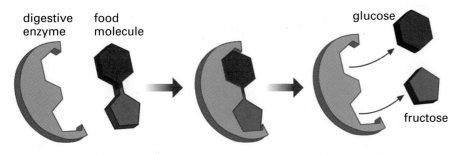

Fig. 14.6 How digestive enzymes work

Based on Fig. 14.6, can you conclude whether the enzymes are used up at the end of a reaction?

Enzymes are specific in their action. This means that each enzyme only works on one type of molecule or a group of similar molecules in a chemical reaction. For example, the enzyme in your saliva only works on starch (found in bread and rice).

Enzymes that help in digestion are called digestive enzymes. The diagram below shows the action of these enzymes during digestion:

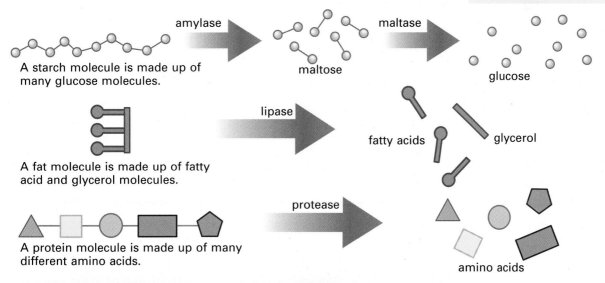

A starch molecule is made up of many glucose molecules.

amylase

maltose

maltase

glucose

A fat molecule is made up of fatty acid and glycerol molecules.

lipase

fatty acids

glycerol

A protein molecule is made up of many different amino acids.

protease

amino acids

Fig. 14.7   Different types of enzymes act on different types of food.

Using Fig. 14.7, can you explain why different types of enzymes are needed to digest different types of food molecules?

14.3 The Digestive System

Which one of the following organisms has a digestive system? How do we identify organisms with digestive systems?

Coral

Starfish

Paramecium

Lady beetle

Snail

Shark

Fig. 14.8 Identify the organisms with digestive systems.

Organisms with digestive systems have two body openings:
- the mouth where the food enters;
- the anus where the undigested food is excreted.

The diagram below shows the human digestive system.

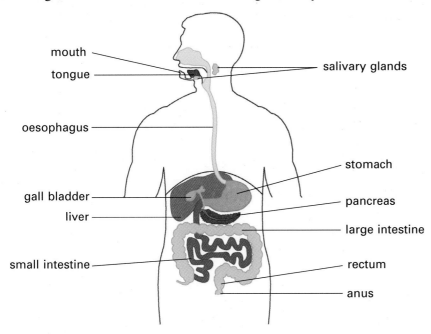

Fig. 14.9 Human digestive system

You will notice that it is made up of the alimentary canal and the related glands. Follow the diagram starting from the mouth. It is one continuous tube that goes all the way from the mouth to the anus.

The alimentary canal consists of the
- mouth;
- oesophagus;
- stomach;
- small intestine;
- large intestine;
- rectum;
- anus.

The glands associated with the alimentary canal include the liver and pancreas, which secrete substances to aid digestion.

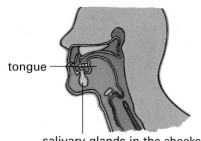

tongue

salivary glands in the cheeks and under the tongue

Fig. 14.10 Mouth

The Mouth

Solid food is physically digested by the chewing action of the teeth in the mouth. It is then rolled into balls by the tongue.

Saliva has a few functions here:
- it contains the digestive enzyme, amylase, to chemically digest starch into simpler sugar, maltose;
- it helps to moisten and lubricate the food.

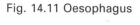

longitudinal muscles

space inside the oesophagus

circular muscles contract, pushing the food forward

food

circular muscles relax, allowing the tube to open wider

Fig. 14.11 Oesophagus

The Oesophagus

The oesophagus is a narrow muscular tube that allows food to move from the mouth to the stomach. The muscles in the wall of the oesophagus contract and relax alternately to push food towards the stomach. Does any chemical digestion take place in the oesophagus?

Try This!

The following model is often used to show how food moves down the oesophagus.

1. Insert a marble into a short piece of rubber tubing with a diameter slightly smaller than that of the marble.

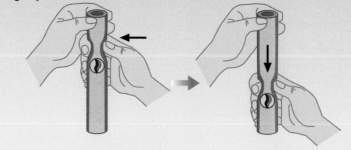

2. Describe how you would squeeze the rubber tubing so that the marble moves down the rubber tubing.

3. Repeat Steps 1 and 2 but apply some oil to the marble.

4. Observe the difference(s) in the movements of the marble with and without oil as it is moved down the rubber tubing. Record the difference(s) in your science portfolio.

The Stomach

The stomach resembles a thick, muscular bag.

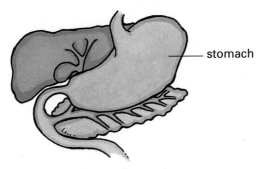

Fig. 14.12 Stomach

The stomach
- has gastric glands which secrete gastric juice (hydrochloric acid and protease) to help in the chemical digestion of proteins;
- physically digests the food by contracting and relaxing its muscular wall to mix the food with gastric juice.

Food can be stored in the stomach for up to four hours. Partially digested food is then released in small amounts into the small intestine.

The Small Intestine

The small intestine is a long coiled structure. In humans, it can stretch up to six metres long!

The glands in the lining of the intestinal walls secrete intestinal juice to completely digest proteins, fats and sugar molecules.

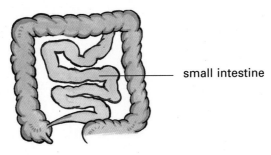

Fig. 14.13 Small intestine

Food in the small intestine is completely digested into simple food molecules that can be absorbed into the bloodstream:

Starch   → maltose → glucose
Fats   → fatty acids and glycerol
Proteins → amino acids

▶ Activity 48-49 P.B.

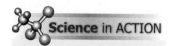

In a very cold environment, Eskimos often eat whale fat.

Before a 100 m sprint race, runners take glucose tablets.

Weightlifters often have diets rich in proteins.

What do you think they take the food for?

The Liver and Gall Bladder

The liver is the largest gland in our body. It secretes an alkaline, greenish-yellow liquid called bile, which

- breaks down the size of fat molecules by physical digestion;
- neutralises the acid from the stomach;
- is stored temporarily in the gall bladder next to the liver and can flow into the small intestines via a tube called the bile duct.

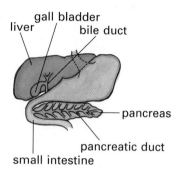

Fig. 14.14 Liver, gall bladder and pancreas

The Pancreas

The pancreas is also a gland that produces pancreatic juice, which
- flows into the small intestine via pancreatic duct;
- contains amylase, lipase and protease to help in digestion.

The Large Intestine

The large intestine is made up of the colon, rectum and anus. It does not take part in the process of digestion, but is essential in removing the undigested food.

The main function of the large intestine is to absorb water and mineral salts from the undigested food material. The undigested food material includes fibre from vegetables.

The undigested matter or faeces is stored temporarily in the rectum until it is passed out through the anus.

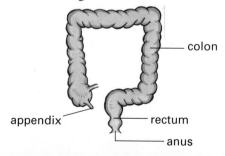

Fig. 14.15 Large intestine

▶ Activity 14 T.W.

Key Points

1. Most food must be digested because their molecules are too large or complex to diffuse through the wall of the small intestine and eventually be absorbed into the bloodstream.

2. Physical or mechanical digestion is the breaking down of food into smaller pieces without changing the chemical structure of the food molecules.

3. Chemical digestion is the breaking down of large complex food molecules into simpler food molecules with the help of enzymes. It changes the chemical structure of the food molecules.

4. Enzymes are special types of proteins produced by our body cells. They speed up the rate of chemical reactions in our body, like those involved in digestion.

5. Digestive enzymes are specific in their actions. For example, amylase breaks down starch into maltose, but has no effect on the digestion of proteins or lipids.

6.

Digestive enzyme	Starting molecule(s)	Product(s)
Amylase	Starch	Maltose
Lipase	Lipids (fats or oils)	Fatty acids and glycerol
Protease	Proteins	Amino acids

7.

Part of the alimentary canal	Secretion found	Enzyme(s) present in secretion	Action of enzyme	Other functions
Mouth	Saliva	Amylase	Breaks down starch into maltose	Teeth break down food into smaller pieces. Tongue rolls food into small balls before swallowing.
Oesophagus	–	–	–	Pushes food into the stomach
Stomach	Gastric juice	Protease	Breaks down long chains of protein into shorter protein chains	Stomach muscles churn up the food when they contract and relax repeatedly.

Part of the alimentary canal	Secretion found	Enzyme(s) present in secretion	Action of enzyme	Other functions
Small intestine	Bile, pancreatic juice, intestinal juice	Amylase	Breaks down starch into maltose	Digested food diffuses through the walls of the small intestine and is eventually absorbed into the bloodstream.
		Lipase	Breaks down lipids into fatty acids and glycerol	
		Protease	Breaks down proteins into amino acids	
Colon	–		–	Most of the water and mineral salts diffuse through the wall of the large intestine into the bloodstream.
Rectum	–		–	Temporarily stores faeces until it is passed out through the anus.
Anus	–		–	Through which faeces is passed out of the body.

8. The end products of digestion are glucose, amino acids, fatty acids and glycerol that are used for cellular processes like respiration, growth and tissue repair.

1. What is digestion?

2. Why is there a need for most food to be digested?

3. What are enzymes?

4.

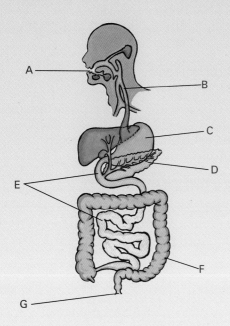

The diagram above shows the digestive system of a human body.

   (a) Name the parts labelled A to G.

   (b) Describe the functions of the parts labelled A to G.

   (c) Name the enzymes that are released in the digestive system. For each of the enzymes, identify the part(s) of the digestive system in which the enzyme is present.

   (d) What is absorbed into the bloodstream in E and F?

   (e) Which part of the body is undigested food passed out from?

5. Name the end products of digestion that are used for respiration.

6. What will happen to an animal if its digestive system malfunctions?

▶**Revision 14 T.W.**

At a GLANCE

Complete the following concept map for this chapter.

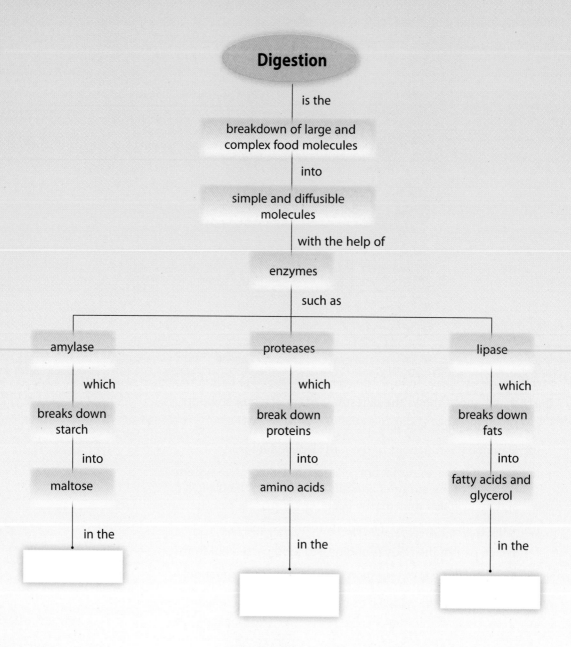

```
                          Digestion

                            is the

                  breakdown of large and
                  complex food molecules

                            into

                   simple and diffusible
                        molecules

                      with the help of

                          enzymes

                          such as

        amylase              proteases              lipase

         which                 which                which

     breaks down           break down           breaks down
        starch               proteins               fats

          into                 into                  into

        maltose            amino acids          fatty acids and
                                                    glycerol

        in the               in the               in the

      [          ]          [          ]         [          ]
```

Besides showing the digestive process on a human figure like in Fig. 14.9, how else can you present it creatively?

1. Fresh fruit should be included in your daily diet but it is unwise to eat only fruit. Why is this so?

2. (a) Explain why is it better to eat an apple than a box of chocolates if you feel hungry in between meals.

   (b) If you are going on a long hike, why is it better to bring chocolate bars than apples?

3. 'An apple a day keeps the doctor away'. Do you agree with this statement? Present your views to the class.

4. A six-month-old baby, fed with small carrot cubes, passed them out in her faeces. Why is that so?

5. Is it possible for food from your mouth to go into the stomach even when your body is upside-down? Explain.

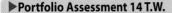

▶**Portfolio Assessment 14 T.W.**

15 Sexual Reproduction in Human Beings

In this chapter, you will learn to:

- recognise that heredity is a process where genetic information is transmitted from one generation to another

- recognise that in sexual reproduction a new individual is formed from the union of an egg and a sperm

- recognise that a new individual formed through sexual reproduction receives genetic information from its mother (via the egg) and its father (via the sperm)

- state some of the physical changes that occur during puberty and early adolescence

- describe briefly the structures and functions of male and female human reproductive systems

- describe briefly the menstrual cycle and fertilisation.

- describe briefly a temporary and a permanent method of birth control

- state the harmful consequences of sexually transmitted diseases like syphilis, gonorrhoea and AIDS

- evaluate the consequences and issues related to abortion and pre-marital sex

- show an appreciation of the social and moral issues relating to abortion and pre-marital sex

- show an appreciation of the need for Singapore to develop our only resource – human resource

Why do some people choose to delay having babies, while others end their pregnancies early?

How does a baby inherit characteristics from his parents...

... from these two types of cells?

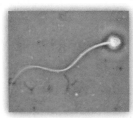 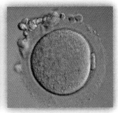

Fig. 15.1 Baby   Fig. 15.2 Sperm   Fig. 15.3 Ovum

What are the issues surrounding sex and pregnancies in our society?

15.1 | Heredity

Study the photographs of some parents with their children. Do the parent and child look alike? What physical characteristics do they have in common?

Fig. 15.4 Parents and their children

Try This!

Compare yourself and/or your sibling with your parents. In what ways are you or your sibling similar to them?

Characteristic	Yourself	Sibling	Father	Mother
Colour of skin				
Colour of hair				
Colour of eyes				
Single/double eyelids				
Attached/free earlobes				

What characteristics have you or your sibling inherited from your parents? If you have a sibling, are the characteristics he/she inherited the same as yours?

▶ Activity 15.3 T.W.

In general, you will look like your parents. You may have your father's black eyes and your mother's curly hair. If you have a sibling, he may have your mother's brown eyes and your father's straight hair instead. Each child has some characteristics of his or her parents.

The characteristics of a person are determined by the genetic information stored in the chromosomes found in the nucleus of the cell.

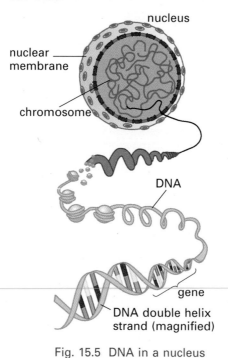

Fig. 15.5 shows the genes that contain information needed to determine a person's physical traits such as the colour of the eyes.

Each cell nucleus has two identical sets of chromosomes. When you were conceived, your father and mother each contributed one set of their chromosomes. So, you received genetic information from both parents.

Fig. 15.5 DNA in a nucleus

Your sibling also received the same sets of chromosomes from your parents. However, the genes are combined differently for him, so he does not look exactly like you. The only exception is if you are identical twins.

> The process of passing on genetic information from one generation to the next is known as **heredity**.

Although your physical characteristics depend on your inherited genes, many of them can be changed by your lifestyle. For example, your height not only depends on your genes, but also on what you eat and whether you exercise.

Fig. 15.6 Siblings look similar but not exactly the same.

15.2 Changes in Puberty

1. Look for a full-sized photograph of yourself which was taken when you were in lower primary and another which was taken recently.

2. Compare your characteristics shown in the two photographs.

3. Record in your science portfolio the physical changes that have taken place.

Have you noticed that some of your school mates have pimples breaking out on their faces or that their voices have deepened?

Before becoming an adult, every adolescent undergoes a period of rapid growth with many physical and emotional changes, known as puberty.

Fig. 15.7 Besides having pimples, teenage boys have to deal with the deepening of their voice.

> **Puberty** is the period of growth in a young adolescent when his or her reproductive organs start to produce sex hormones and mature sex cells. Puberty often starts at the age of 10 to 12 in girls and 12 to 14 in boys.

You know your puberty has begun when you notice several physical changes in your body, like your height increasing rapidly, or hair growing in the armpits. Look at your classmates around you. Can you identify who has undergone puberty? In what other ways is he or she physically 'different' from others?

Fig. 15.8 Who has begun puberty around you?

The physical changes during puberty are set off by sex hormones.

> **Hormones** are chemicals produced and released by organs, known as hormonal glands, in the human body. They are responsible for causing physical and chemical changes in our body.

When you reach puberty, your body will prepare itself for reproduction by releasing sex hormones into the bloodstream. These sex hormones are responsible for the physical and emotional changes that happen to you, like the growth spurts.

▶ **Activity 15.2 T.W.**

For the Boys

During puberty in boys, the male reproductive organs will become active. The following changes will take place:

- Male sex hormones and cells will be produced;
- Hair on the face, pubic regions, armpits and chest will start to grow;
- The body will become more muscular;
- The shoulders will broaden;
- The male sex organ (penis) will enlarge;
- Voice will break and deepen;
- More sexually interested in girls.

Fig. 15.9 Puberty in boys

For the Girls

During puberty in girls, the female reproductive organs will become active. The following changes will take place:

- Female sex hormones and cells will be produced;
- Hair at the pubic regions and armpits will start to grow;
- The breasts will grow bigger;
- The hips will broaden to become wider and rounder;
- Menstruation will start;
- More sexually interested in the boys.

Fig. 15.10 Puberty in girls

15.3 Male and Female Human Reproductive Systems

The male and female reproductive systems are primarily different but they are able to complement each other to achieve a common goal – reproduction.

Let us look at each system in detail.

Male Reproductive System

The diagram below shows the structure of a male reproductive system.

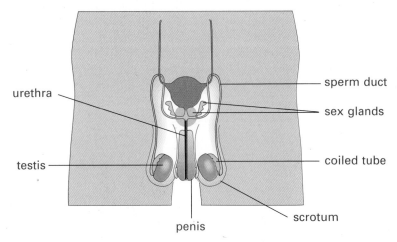

urethra

sperm duct

sex glands

coiled tube

testis

scrotum

penis

Fig. 15.11 Male reproductive system

Testis (plural: testes)
- male reproductive organ
- produces sperms and sex hormones from puberty onwards

Coiled tube (epididymis)
- stores sperms before they enter sperm duct

Sperm duct (vas deferens)
- long tube that carries the sperms to the urethra

Urethra
- carries the sperms through the penis to outside the body
- also transports urine from the bladder to the penis

Scrotum
- sac that holds the testes outside the body where they can be kept cool

Sex glands
- release fluid that nourishes the sperms with energy to swim
- mixture of fluid and sperms is called semen, which leaves the penis through the urethra

Penis
- male sex organ
- made up of muscles
- ejects the sperms into the vagina during sexual intercourse

Male sex cell or sperm

A **sperm** is a male sex cell produced in the testes. It moves by lashing its tail. A healthy male adult produces about two billion sperms in his testes every day.

Study the diagram on the left which shows the structure of a sperm.

Describe the structure of a sperm.

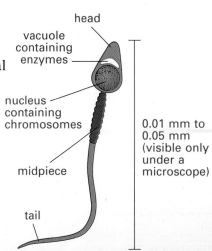

head

vacuole containing enzymes

nucleus containing chromosomes

midpiece

0.01 mm to 0.05 mm (visible only under a microscope)

tail

Fig. 15.12 A sperm

Female Reproductive System

The following diagram shows the structure of a female reproductive system.

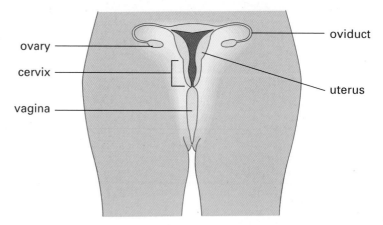

Fig. 15.13 Female reproductive system

Ovary
- female reproductive organ
- produces eggs and sex hormones

Uterus (womb)
- pear-shaped
- site where foetus develops during pregnancy

Oviduct (Fallopian tube)
- mature egg travels along this tube towards the uterus

Cervix
- narrow neck of the uterus
- widens during childbirth for the baby to come out of the uterus

Vagina
- birth canal
- muscular tube leading from the cervix to the outside of the female body
- sperms are deposited here during intercourse
- widens during childbirth to make way for the baby

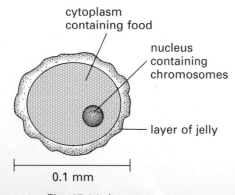

Fig. 15.14 An ovum

Female sex cell or ovum

An egg or **ovum** (plural: ova) is a female sex cell released from an ovary. Unlike the sperm, the ovum cannot move by itself. A mature ovum is released by one of the two ovaries about once in every 28 days.

Study the diagram on the left which shows the structure of an ovum.

Describe the structure of an ovum.

▶Activity 15.1 T.W.　　▶Activity 50 P.B.

15.4 The Menstrual Cycle

When a girl reaches puberty, a mature ovum will be released from an ovary every month for reproduction. The release of a mature ovum from an ovary is called **ovulation**. If the ovum is not fertilised, it will be discharged from the body together with blood and broken uterine lining. The discharge of blood, broken uterine lining and dead ovum from the body is called **menstruation**.

Study the chart illustrating the menstrual cycle. Can you determine how many days a menstrual cycle often lasts?

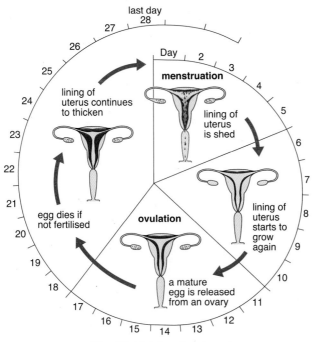

Fig. 15.15 Menstrual cycle

The menstrual cycle usually repeats every 28 days. However, the length of the cycle may vary between 21 to 35 days.

Day **1** to Day **5**	• Menstruation starts • Broken uterine lining, dead ovum and blood are discharged from the vagina • Menstruation may last for three to five days
Day **6** to Day **10**	• Menstruation stops • Uterine lining starts to grow and thicken again
Day **11** to Day **17**	• Uterine lining continues to thicken • Ovulation starts about Day 14
Day **18** to Day **28**	• Uterine lining continues to thicken • Uterine lining is filled with blood vessels to prepare for fertilised egg to implant and develop in it • If no fertilisation happens, the ovum will disintegrate when it reaches the uterus and menstruation will occur

Science NUGGET

Some females get moody and irritable a few days before their menstruation begins. This condition is referred to as pre-menstrual tension (PMT).

Women stop menstruating when they are about 50 years old. This is called menopause and it marks the end of their fertility.

Connect

Females should maintain a high standard of personal hygiene when they menstruate to stay healthy and keep away from possible infections.

Exploring Further

The period starting three days before ovulation to three days after ovulation is called the fertile phase of the menstrual cycle. Why is this period called the 'fertile phase'?

Try This!

1. What is a menstrual cycle? Why is a female unable to predict exactly when menstruation will occur?

2. State the difference between menstruation and ovulation.

3. Will menstruation stop if ovulation stops?

4. Name the substances discharged during menstruation.

5. Why do some females faint during menstruation?

15.5 Fertilisation

Fig. 15.16 Fertilisation

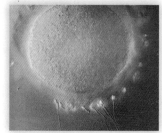

Fig. 15.17 Sperms clustering around an egg

Fig. 15.16 shows the union of two cells in sexual reproduction. Name the two cells.

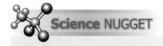

Science NUGGET

If there is no egg in the Fallopian tubes, the sperms will die two or three days later.

During sexual intercourse, millions of sperms are deposited by the penis of a male into the vagina of a female. From the vagina, the sperms swim their way up through the cervix, into the uterus and finally into the Fallopian tubes. If a sperm meets an egg in the Fallopian tube, fertilisation may occur. Although millions of sperms are released into the vagina, only one will fertilise the egg.

When a sperm enters the egg, the egg will release a chemical that prevents other sperms from entering the egg.

In the egg, the nucleus of the sperm fuses with the nucleus of the egg to form a fertilised egg. The fusion of the two nuclei is called **fertilisation**.

The fertilised egg or zygote then moves along the fallopian tube to the uterus where it will attach itself to the thickened lining of the uterus. Over the next nine months, it will gradually develop into a baby.

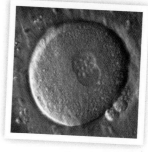

Fig. 15.18 The nuclei of the sperm and egg fusing during fertilisation

1st month
(about 0.8 cm long)

The embryo is growing some basic physical features that are recognisable, like the leg bud and heart bulge. Eyes and ears are also starting to form. The heart is already pumping blood and beating at twice the adult's heart rate.

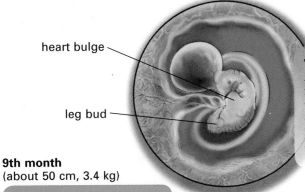

heart bulge

leg bud

9th month
(about 50 cm, 3.4 kg)

By now, the baby has reached full term and is a little human being. She has put on a lot of weight. In two weeks' time, the baby will descend into a head down position, ready to face the world outside!

Newborn baby

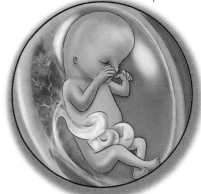

3rd month
(about 8 cm, 43 g)

It is officially a foetus! Major organs like the heart and brain are formed. The foetus can make a fist with its fingers and can even feel pain. The fingernails and toenails are forming too. She can squint, frown, and grimace. She can grasp now, too, and she may be able to suck her thumb.

6th month
(about 38 cm, 1 kg)

The foetus is covered with fine hair. She can hear her mother's voice and is very active. She will kick and make facial expressions. Soon, she will be able to open her eyes!

Fig. 15.19 Miracle of life – foetal development

Some facts about breast milk and breastfeeding:

- A newborn can be breastfed as soon as he is born.
- Babies can be fed on just breast milk (no water) for the first six months.
- First milk (colostrum) is yellow and packed with antibodies to protect the newborn from infections.
- Breast milk has special ingredients that help in maximum brain development.
- Commercial formulas can never match up to breast milk as breast milk has the right balance of nutrients and antibodies and is easier to digest.

15.6 Birth Control

Some married couples practise birth control or contraception to plan their pregnancies. What do you think are the reasons behind their decisions?

Birth control or contraceptive methods prevent pregnancies by applying one or more of the following methods:

- **Preventing ovulation**
  The development and release of the egg are suppressed or stopped using certain hormones.

- **Preventing the flow of sperms to the penis**
  The flow of sperms from the testes to the urethra and the penis is stopped or blocked by cutting and removing a section of the sperm duct.

- **Preventing fertilisation**
  Sperm and egg are prevented from meeting each other.

- **Preventing implantation**
  The fertilised egg is prevented from implanting onto the lining of the uterus.

Contraceptive methods are not entirely foolproof and all of them carry a certain amount of risk of unwanted pregnancy.

Contraceptive methods can be classified into two main groups according to their effects on their users – temporary contraceptive methods and permanent contraceptive methods.

Temporary Contraceptive Method

Temporary contraceptive methods are those which allow couples to have children as and when the couples stop using these methods.

One example is the use of condoms. There are male condoms and female condoms. Both prevent the sperms from coming into contact with the egg physically, thus preventing fertilisation.

Fig. 15.20 Female condom   Fig. 15.21 Male condoms

There are also other devices or substances being used, as shown in the photographs below.

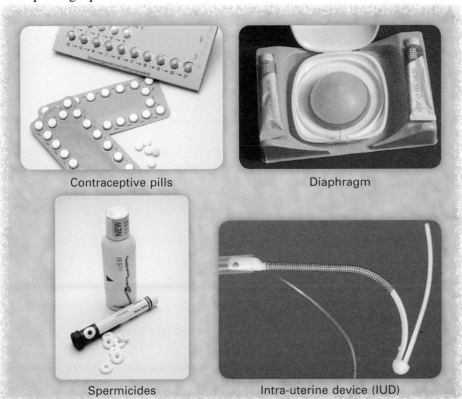

Contraceptive pills   Diaphragm

Spermicides   Intra-uterine device (IUD)

Fig. 15.22 Some temporary contraceptive devices or substances that are used

Find out how the devices or substances shown above are used to prevent pregnancies.

Permanent Contraceptive Methods

Permanent contraceptive methods are those which prevent their users from having any more children once these methods have been applied.

These methods are suitable if a man or woman is absolutely sure that they do not want any more children in the future. This is because once the permanent contraceptive methods are applied, they are *almost* impossible to be reversed.

Permanent contraceptive methods involve the permanent removal of a person's reproductive capabilities by a process called **sterilisation**.

Male sterilisation or vasectomy

A section of the sperm duct is cut and tied to prevent the flow of sperms to the urethra and the penis. Semen from a sterilised male will then contain only the fluid from the sex glands without any sperm. See Fig. 15.23.

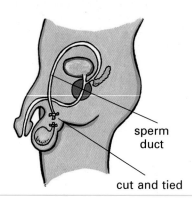

Fig. 15.23 Vasectomy

Female sterilisation or ligation

The mid-portion of both Fallopian tubes are cut and their ends are tied to prevent the eggs that are released by the ovaries from reaching the uterus. See Fig. 15.24.

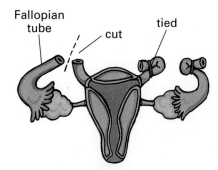

Fig. 15.24 Ligation

Why do doctors often recommend temporary contraceptive methods to young married couples? When do doctors recommend permanent contraceptive methods?

15.7 Pre-marital Sex and Abortion

Pre-marital sex is engaging in sexual intercourse before marriage.

What are the consequences of engaging in pre-marital sex?

Try This!

1. Your teacher will divide your class into two groups.

2. One group is assigned to gather information on the social issues and consequences related to pre-marital sex (e.g. physical and mental health risks).

3. The other group is assigned to gather information on the moral issues and consequences related to pre-marital sex (e.g. the different views of different cultures and religions on the morality of pre-marital sex).

4. Present and discuss the information gathered by your group with the class.

5. Record the findings of your discussion in your science portfolio.

Some people are not mentally ready to have a baby, so when they are pregnant, they terminate the pregnancy by undergoing abortion.

> Oh no! I'm still so young and I'm not ready to be a mother! What should I do?

Abortion is the deliberate ending or termination of a pregnancy. It involves the removal of the developing foetus from the mother's uterus. An abortion carried out after the first three months of pregnancy poses a great risk to the mother's health.

Fig. 15.25 Pregnant teenager

Try This!

1. Your teacher will divide your class into two groups.

2. One group of students is assigned to gather all the medical reasons for or against abortion.

3. The other group of students is assigned to gather all the social reasons for or against abortion.

4. Present and discuss the information gathered by your group with the class.

5. Record the findings of your discussion in your science portfolio.

Should abortion be used as a way to deal with unwanted pregnancies? Would the adoption of the baby from the unwanted pregnancy be a better solution?

As abortion is a serious matter, those involved should seek advice from professionals such as counsellors and doctors. Abortion should only be carried out by a trained medical personnel, under safe and proper conditions such as in a hospital where adequate medical attention and equipment are available.

Even with the best medical attention, abortion can have complications. The table below shows some of the physical and mental health risks of having an abortion.

Physical health risks	Mental health risks
• Heavy bleeding • Infection • Continued pregnancy • Infertility • Death	• Guilt • Sense of loss • Sadness • Depression • Suicidal thoughts • Difficulty in maintaining relationships

Table 15.1 Some physical and mental health risks of abortion

What are the other physical and mental health risks of having an abortion?

Exploring Further

1. Express your views on whether unmarried couples should have pre-marital sex.

2. What are the dangers of having pre-marital sex?

3. Why does pre-marital sex often lead to abortion?

4. Why is abortion not allowed for mothers at an advanced stage of pregnancy?

15.8 Sexually Transmitted Infections (STIs)

Sexually transmitted infections (STIs) are infections which are passed from an infected person to others through sexual contact. They affect mainly the reproductive organs, but can also spread to other parts of the body.

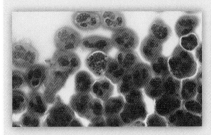
Gonorrhoea–causing bacteria

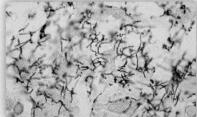
Spiral bacteria which cause syphilis

Human Immunodeficiency Virus (HIV) infecting white blood cells

Fig. 15.26 Some bacteria and viruses that cause STIs

The above photographs show the different types of micro-organisms like bacteria and viruses that cause sexually transmitted infections such as syphilis, gonorrhoea and AIDS (Acquired Immune Deficiency Syndrome). How can a person be infected with the above micro-organisms and virus?

How would you know if a person has STIs? The answer is that you don't!

STIs are dangerous because a person infected with certain STIs does not show any signs or symptoms until the later stage of the infection. Before he becomes very sick, he might have unknowingly infected other people.

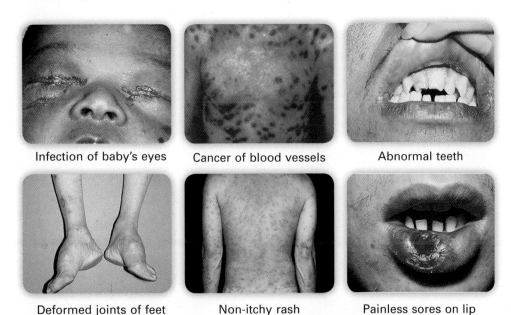

Infection of baby's eyes   Cancer of blood vessels   Abnormal teeth

Deformed joints of feet   Non-itchy rash   Painless sores on lip

Fig. 15.27 Can you identify the STI responsible for each sign?

▶ Activity 15.4 T.W.

The following chart lists the causes and harmful consequences of three STIs.

Sexually transmitted infections

Gonorrhoea

caused by

gonorrhoea-causing bacteria

transmitted during

sexual contact with an infected person or passed from an infected mother to her baby at birth

with harmful consequences

in babies:
• blindness at birth

in females:
• lower abdominal pain caused by infected Fallopian tube
• sterility

in males:
• pain when passing urine
• discharge of pus from penis

Syphilis

caused by

spiral bacteria

transmitted during

sexual contact with an infected person or passed from an infected mother to her baby at birth

with harmful consequences

in babies:
• born deaf
• born with deformed teeth and bones

in adults:
during early stages
• painless sores
• non-itchy rash

during late stages
• deformed joints
• paralysis
• insanity
• death

Acquired Immune Deficiency Syndrome (AIDS)

caused by

Human Immunodeficiency Virus (HIV)

transmitted during

sexual contact with an infected person, passed from an infected mother to her baby at birth, or the entry of HIV-infected blood into a person's body through blood transfusion or sharing of needles

with harmful consequences

in babies, children and adults:
during early stages
• loss of weight
• prolonged fever
• loss of appetite
• serious diarrhoea
• night sweat

during late stages
• pneumonia
• brain infection
• Kaposi's sarcoma
• death

Here are some truths about STIs:

- STIs are transmitted through body fluids: vaginal secretion, semen, blood, breast milk and saliva;
- STIs can be transmitted without having sexual intercourse. For example, skin-to-skin contact or genital rubbing can transmit Human Papillomavirus (HPV) and the herpes virus;
- When diagnosed early, the majority of STIs can be cured or treated to relieve the symptoms;
- The chances of contracting and transmitting STIs cannot be totally eliminated even with the use of condoms.

Prevention and Protection

Is there a way to prevent getting STIs?

Using a condom is a way to reduce the risk of transmitting and contracting STIs, as it reduces the chances of exchanging body fluids. The most effective way to prevent getting STIs, however, is to abstain from sex before marriage and to stay faithful to your spouse whom you know is STI-free.

Are there any other methods that can be used to protect yourself against STIs?

Teenagers comprise nearly four million of the 15 million cases of sexually transmitted infections (STIs) estimated to occur annually in the United States of America.

In 2006, the number of Singaporean teenagers with STIs was more than twice the number in 2002. In the same year, about one-fifth of new HIV infections affected people aged 20-29. Some of them may have even had the infection when they were teenagers and not know about it until several years later.

Discuss with your friends the best ways to educate teenagers on the risks of STIs.

Key Points

1. Heredity is a process where genetic information is passed from one generation to another.

2. A new individual formed from the union of an egg and a sperm receives genetic information from its mother via the egg and from its father via the sperm.

3. Puberty is the stage of growth in an adolescent when his or her reproductive organs start to produce sex hormones and sex cells.

4. Changes during puberty caused by sex hormones produced by the testes and the ovaries are summarised in the table below.

Boy	Girl
• Testes produce sperms and sex hormones. • Height increases rapidly. • Shoulders widen, body becomes muscular and penis enlarges. • Hair grows at pubic region and in the armpits. It may also grow on the chest and the face. • Voice deepens as voice box enlarges.	• Ovaries release mature eggs and produce sex hormones. • Height increases rapidly. • Breasts grow bigger, hips become wider and rounder. • Hair grows at the pubic region and in the armpits. • Menstruation starts.

5. A male human reproductive system:

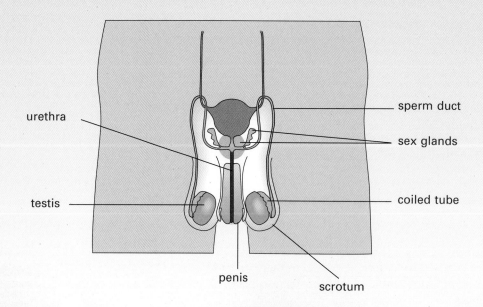

6. A female human reproductive system:

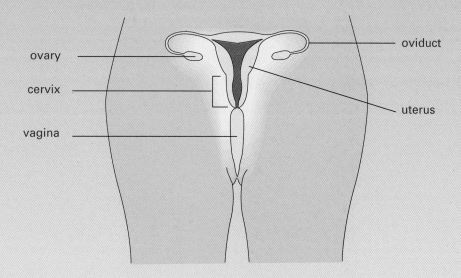

7. The release of a mature ovum from an ovary is called ovulation.

8. The discharge of blood, broken uterine lining and dead ovum from the body is called menstruation.

9. The menstrual cycle involves ovulation and menstruation. It repeats itself about every 28 days.

10. Fertilisation is the fusion of the nuclei of a sperm and an egg.

11. Birth control or contraception involves processes to prevent or stop pregnancies by preventing ovulation, fertilisation, or the development of a fertilised egg.

12. Temporary contraceptive methods allow couples to have children when they stop using these methods.

13. Spermicides, condoms, diaphragms, contraceptive pills and IUDs are used in temporary contraceptive methods.

14. Vasectomy and ligation are permanent contraceptive methods which, when applied, will not allow married couples to have any more children in the future.

15. Engaging in sexual intercourse before marriage is called pre-marital sex. It can lead to unplanned pregnancies and STIs.

16. Abortion is the deliberate ending of a pregnancy by removing the developing foetus from the mother's uterus.

17. Sexually transmitted infections or STIs are infections which are passed from an infected person to others through sexual contact. They include gonorrhoea, syphilis and AIDS.

let's Review!

1. Why are your looks in many ways, like your parents?

2. (a) State the changes in male and female adolescents during puberty.

   (b) What causes these changes?

3. The diagrams below show the structures of the male and female human reproductive systems.

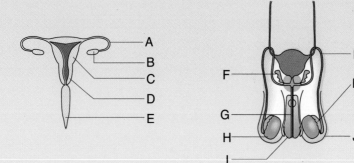

   (a) Name the structures labelled A to L in the diagrams above.

   (b) Briefly describe the functions of each of the labelled structures.

4. Briefly describe the following:

   (a) Menstrual cycle

   (b) Fertilisation

5. Give an example of a

   (a) temporary contraceptive method;

   (b) permanent contraceptive method.

   Describe how each of the above methods works.

6. State an advantage and a disadvantage of practising birth control in family planning.

7. (a) What is pre-marital sex?

   (b) Why should we avoid pre-marital sex?

8. (a) What is an abortion?

   (b) What are the side-effects of having an abortion?

9. (a) What are sexually transmitted infections or STIs?

   (b) Name an STI caused by bacteria. Describe the harmful consequences suffered by a person infected with the STI.

10. What happens to a person who suffers from AIDS?

▶**Revision 15 T.W.**

Study the concept map shown below.

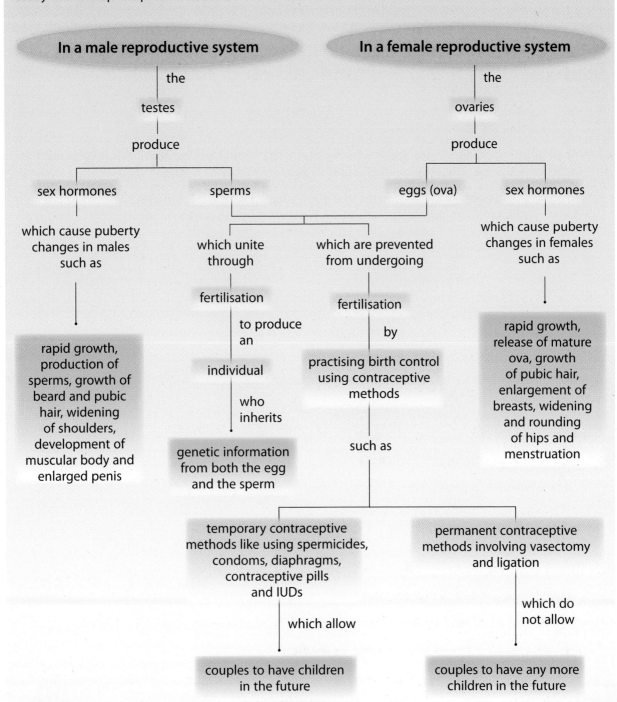

In a male reproductive system

the

testes

produce

sex hormones

sperms

which cause puberty changes in males such as

rapid growth, production of sperms, growth of beard and pubic hair, widening of shoulders, development of muscular body and enlarged penis

which unite through

fertilisation

to produce an

individual

who inherits

genetic information from both the egg and the sperm

which are prevented from undergoing

fertilisation

by

practising birth control using contraceptive methods

such as

In a female reproductive system

the

ovaries

produce

eggs (ova)

sex hormones

which cause puberty changes in females such as

rapid growth, release of mature ova, growth of pubic hair, enlargement of breasts, widening and rounding of hips and menstruation

temporary contraceptive methods like using spermicides, condoms, diaphragms, contraceptive pills and IUDs

which allow

couples to have children in the future

permanent contraceptive methods involving vasectomy and ligation

which do not allow

couples to have any more children in the future

Draw a concept map to show the consequences of engaging in pre-marital sex, which may include abortion and contracting STIs.

Think Tank

1. Nowadays the government encourages married couples to have more than two children. In your opinion, how many children should a married couple have in their family? Discuss why it is important for Singaporeans to have bigger families.

2. (a) Some people are ashamed to see a doctor for their STIs and try to get their own drugs at the pharmacy instead. They may unknowingly get the wrong drugs or take the drugs incorrectly. What are the dangers of doing this?

   (b) The likelihood of infection with STIs is increased by having more than one sexual partner. What are the reasons for this?

3. There is an on-going debate about whether teenagers should get consent from their parents for abortion. What are your views on this? Support your answer with reasons.

4. Imagine you are one of the classmates of a pupil infected with AIDS. You are supposed to attend a forum to discuss issues concerning this pupil. What would you say at the forum?

IT Links

Visit www.mygir.com for easy reference to the following websites:

Chapter	IT Links
1 Science as an Inquiry	• Find out about safety in the laboratory: http://www.chem.vt.edu/RVGS/ACT/lab/safety_rules.html • View and understand laboratory safety rules: http://www.chem.unl.edu/safety/hslabcon.html • Do you know the scientific method well? Try a very short activity at: http://www.quia.com/rd/7331.html
2 Science and Technology in Society	• Read about different abuses in various areas of science where the American public can report abuses of science to the Union of Concerned Scientists (UCS). Read about how UCS can help to prevent further abuse: http://www.ucsusa.org/scientific_integrity/interference/specific-examples-of-the-abuse-of-science.html
3 Use of Measuring Instruments	• How to read a metric measurement using a ruler or scale — Interactive game: http://www.funbrain.com/funbrain/measure/ • Measuring length — Interactive quiz: http://www.bbc.co.uk/skillswise/numbers/measuring/lwc/quiz.shtml • Measuring length — Interactive activity: http://www.graphics.cornell.edu/outreach/java/ruler/ • Vernier scale — Interactive activity: http://www.upscale.utoronto.ca/PVB/Harrison/Vernier/Vernier.html • Calculating volume: www.nyu.edu/pages/mathmol/textbook/volume.html • Interactive online activities that are used to find the volume of an object: www.nyu.edu/pages/mathmol/modules/water/dpart1.html
4 Physical Quantities and Units	• What is the difference between weight and mass? What is your weight on other planets of the solar system? http://www.exploratorium.edu/ronh/weight/index.html • Convert one unit to another! http://www.digitaldutch.com/unitconverter • Are you able to identify a fresh egg and a rotten egg without breaking them? The following website may give you a clue: http://www.explorelearning.com/index.cfm?method=cResource.dspView&ResourceID=362
5 Classification of Matter	• Learn about the characteristics of materials and try the activity at home! http://www.channel4learning.net/sites/essentials/science/material/charmaterials_bi.jsp • Try these interactive activities to test the physical properties of different materials: http://www.bbc.co.uk/schools/scienceclips/ages/7_8/characteristics_materials.shtml http://www.pbs.org/wgbh/buildingbig/lab/materials.html

6	Elements, Compounds and Mixtures	• Learn how the Periodic Table came about: http://www.sciencebyjones.com/periodic_table1.htm
		• Play an online game to learn the Periodic Table – by name or symbol: http://www.funbrain.com/funbrain/periodic/
		• Try a simple interactive activity to differentiate elements, compounds and mixtures on the following website: http://www.darvill.clara.net/hotpots/emc.htm
7	Separation Techniques	• Learn how to pan for gold in this website: http://imnh.isu.edu/digitalatlas/teach/lsnplns/goldpnlp.htm
		• Learn how to use paper chromatography for forensic identification of ink samples: http://www.yesmag.bc.ca/projects/paper_chromaBW.html
		• Watch the NEWater process at: http://www.pub.gov.sg/NEWater_files/newater_tech/index.html
8	Solutions and Suspensions	• Read about the properties of acids and alkalis in this webpage: http://www.lausd.k12.ca.us/Carnegie_MS/Sarmiento/science/experiments/acidsbasessalts.html
		• Learn how to prepare an indicator using cabbage: http://www.cupertino.k12.ca.us/westvalley.www/programs/natural_science/4thGrade/cabbage.htm
		• Play a matching game! http://www.quia.com/mc/50890.html
		• Learn more about solutions and suspensions in the following sites: http://dbhs.wvusd.k12.ca.us/webdocs/Solutions/Intro-to-Solutions.html http://www.800mainstreet.com/9/0009-001-mix-solut.html
		• Are there other pH indicators that are not mentioned in the textbook? Learn about other pH indicators from the following websites: http://www.101science.com/PH.html http://en.wikipedia.org/wiki/PH_indicator
9	Classification of Plant and Animal Life	• Try an interactive activity to sort living things into animals or plants: http://www.bbc.co.uk/schools/scienceclips/ages/6_7/variation_fs.shtml
		• What is taxonomy? http://www.nhptv.org/natureworks/nweptaxonomy.htm
		• Learn more about the different classes of animals: http://www.kidport.com/RefLib/Science/Animals/Animals.htm
10	Cells – Structure, Function and Organisation	• Read and understand the articles that describe cells and try the online quiz! http://www.cellsalive.com/toc.htm
		• Learn more about your amazing body at the following website: http://www.bupa.co.uk/health_information/html/organ/
		• Learn more about the different systems in our body with a virtual tour: http://www.medtropolis.com/VBody.asp
11	Particulate Model of Matter	• Test your knowledge on solids, liquids and gases in this interactive website: http://www.bbc.co.uk/schools/gcsebitesize/gigaflat/chemistry/particlesf/particlesf_quiz.shtml
		• See how particles in a gas behave in this simulation: http://home.comcast.net/~aosowiecki/Simulations/KineticModel.html
		• See how temperature affects the speed of gas in this website: http://www.colorado.edu/physics/2000/bec/temperature.html

12	Simple Concepts of Atoms and Molecules	• View and understand the interesting graphics that explain the properties of atoms and molecules: http://education.jlab.org/atomtour/
		• Learn more about atoms and molecules in: http://www.etap.org/demo/grade5_science/instruction1tutor.html
13	Transport in Living Things	• Click to view the different systems in the human body: http://www.kidshealth.org/kid/closet/movies/how_the_body_works_interim.html
		• Explore the transport systems in the human body: http://sln2.fi.edu/biosci/systems/systems.html
14	Digestion in Animals	• Read a story on the human digestive system from each of the following websites: http://yucky.kids.discovery.com/flash/body/pg000126.html http://www.kidshealth.org/kid/body/digest_noSW.html
15	Sexual Reproduction in Human Beings	• Learn more about genes here: http://www.kidshealth.org/teen/diseases_conditions/genetic/genes_genetic_disorders.html
		• How many of the infectious or transmissible diseases listed on the following website are you unaware of? How does the listing of infectious diseases on the website benefit you, your family, community and country? http://www.health.vic.gov.au/ideas/diseases/quicklinks.htm
		• How many of the non-infectious or non-transmissible diseases listed on the following website are you unaware of? How does the listing of non-infectious diseases on the website benefit you, your family, community and country? http://patientlinx.com/
		• Learn more about your sexual health here: http://kidshealth.org/teen/sexual_health/

Glossary

A

Abortion: the deliberate ending of a pregnancy by removing the developing foetus from the mother's uterus and should only be carried out by trained medical personnel

Acid: has a sour taste, turns blue litmus red, reacts with some metals to produce hydrogen, reacts with carbonates to produce carbon dioxide and reacts with alkalis to form salts. E.g. hydrochloric acid and carbonic acid

Active transport: a process that uses energy from the respiration of a plant

Acquired Immune Deficiency Syndrome (AIDS): a disease caused by the Human Immunodeficiency Virus (HIV)

Alimentary canal: human digestive tract

Alkali: has a bitter taste and a soapy feeling, turns red litmus blue and reacts with dilute acids to form salts

Amino acids: individual, simple units of protein

Ampere (A): the SI unit for electric current

Amphibian: a cold-blooded animal that can live both on land and in the water. E.g. frogs and salamanders

Amylase: enzyme that breaks down starch into small sugar molecules in the mouth and small intestine

Animal: a multicellular organism that cannot produce food, is mobile and has to take in food

Anus: the opening at the end of the alimentary canal through which faeces is excreted

Aqueous solution: a solution in which water is the solvent

Arachnid: an invertebrate covered with an exoskeleton, has four pairs of jointed legs and a body segmented into two parts

Area: a measure of the size or extent of a surface

Arthropod: an animal with a segmented body, jointed legs and exoskeleton. E.g. spider, lobster, centipede and insects

Atom: the smallest particle of an element that can exist. Atoms are so small that they can only be seen under electron microscopes.

Average speed: total amount of distance travelled over total amount of time taken

B

Base quantity: a physical quantity that is not made up of other base quantities

Base unit: unit of a base quantity

Bird: a warm-blooded vertebrate covered with feathers, has a beak and a pair of wings

Birth control (contraception): a process of preventing pregnancies by preventing fertilisation, ovulation or the development of a fertilised egg

Blood circulatory system: transports substances around the body

Boiling: occurs when a liquid changes into a gas at its boiling point

Boiling point: the temperature at which the substance changes from liquid to gas

C

Cell: basic unit of living things

Cell membrane: a partially permeable membrane around a cell

Chloroplast: tiny disc-like structure in a plant cell containing a green substance called chlorophyll

Chromosome: thread-like structure in the nucleus of a cell storing chemical instructions needed to build the cell, control its functions and determine its structure

Cytoplasm: jelly-like substance in cells where chemical reactions take place

Cervix: narrow neck of the uterus

Chemical digestion: the breakdown of large food molecules into smaller ones. It involves chemical reactions.

Chemical formula: shows the number and kinds of atoms in each molecule. E.g. H_2 denotes a hydrogen molecule which consists of two hydrogen atoms

Chemical reaction: involves changes in matter due to the rearrangement of atoms or molecules. When it occurs, energy is usually taken in or given out. However, the number of each type of atom before and after a chemical reaction remains equal. Morever, new substances are also formed. E.g. decomposition and oxidation

Chromatography: a technique used to separate dyes

Classification: the grouping of objects into sets according to one or more common properties

Cloning: the replication of cells

Coiled tube (epididymis): a tube connecting the rear of the testis to the sperm duct

Compound: a substance that is made up of more than two elements chemically combined together

Condom: a fine rubber or plastic sheath pulled over the erect penis or inserted into the vagina to stop the semen from entering the uterus

Corrosion: the interaction of a material with the environment that leads to the deterioration of physical properties. Rust, for example, is formed when iron interacts with oxygen and water.

Cubic metre: SI unit of volume

D

Density: mass per unit volume

Desalination: a technique to remove salt and other waste particles from seawater

Deoxyribonucleic acid (DNA): a material that makes up genes found in the chromosomes of a cell; shaped like a double helix linked by four kinds of chemical bases

Dichotomous key: a chart that classifies objects by dividing them into two smaller groups at each stage

Diffusion: the movement of molecules from a region of higher concentration to a region of lower concentration

Digestive enzyme: an enzyme that helps in digestion

Digestive system: breaks down food into simpler substances for absorption

Dilute solution: containing a large amount of solvent, usually water

Distillation: used to separate a solvent from a solution; a method of separating miscible liquids

Distillate: the solvent obtained from distillation

Ductile: can be drawn into wires

E

Electric current: the rate of flow of electric charges

Electrical conductor: a material that allows electricity to pass through readily

Electrical conductivity: a measure of how readily an electric current flows through the material

Electrical insulator: a material that does not allow electricity to pass through readily

Electrons: negatively charged particles in an atom

Element: a substance that cannot be split into two or more simpler substances by chemical reactions

Embryo: fertilised egg

Evaporation: used to separate solutes from a solvent

F

Faeces: undigested food

Female reproductive system: produces eggs for reproduction

Fertilisation: the fusion of the nuclei of a sperm and an egg

Filtrate: the liquid that passes through the filter during filtration

Filtration: a process used to separate the insoluble solid from the liquid in a suspension. A filter is used to trap the solid residue while the liquid that passes through the filter is known as the filtrate.

Fish: a cold-blooded vertebrate which has gills to breathe and fins to swim in the water

Flexibility: the ability of a material to bend without breaking

Foetus: a developing unborn human after major structures and organs are developed, usually three months after fertilisation

G

Gall bladder: bile is stored here temporarily before being released into the small intestines

Gastric juice: digestive juice from the stomach

Genetically-modified food: food that is specially grown by altering a gene; food that is produced from organisms that are genetically altered

Glucose: the simplest form of sugar that can be absorbed by our body and is utilised in respiration for the release of energy

Glycerol: a sweet syrupy hygroscopic trihydroxyl alcohol $C_3H_8O_3$, usually obtained by the saponification of fats and used especially as a solvent and plasticiser

Gonorrhoea: a sexually transmitted disease which is caused by infectious bacteria. It can cause sterility in infected women and blindness in newborn babies.

H

Hardness: the ability of a material to withstand scratches and wear

Heredity: the transmission of genetic information from one generation to another

Hormone: chemical released by glands in the human body

Human Immunodeficiency Virus (HIV): a virus which is transmitted via exchange of bodily fluids and causes AIDS

Homogeneous solution: a solution with the same colour, density, appearance and other physical and chemical properties in every part of the solution

I

Implantation: happens when the embryo attaches itself to the wall of the uterus after ferilisation

Indicator: a chemical that can tell us whether a substance is acidic or alkaline in nature by its colour change. E.g. litmus

Insect: an invertebrate covered with an exoskeleton, has three pairs of jointed legs and body segmented into three parts

Integrated process skills: a combination of basic process skills

Intra-uterine device (IUD): a coil of metal or plastics that is inserted inside the uterus to prevent the lining of the uterus from thickening in preparation for the implantation of a zygote

Invertebrate: an animal without a backbone. E.g. insects and worms

K

Kelvin: SI unit for temperature

Kilogram: SI unit for mass

L

Large intestines: a part of the digestive system that absorbs water from undigested food

Length: the distance between two points

Ligation: female sterilisation which involves the surgical removal of the mid-portion of both Fallopian tubes and then clipping their open ends

Lipase: enzyme that breaks down fats into fatty acids and glycerol in the small intestine

Liver: an organ that is also the largest gland in the human body. It secretes bile to aid the digestion of fats

M

Magnetic force: the force of attraction or repulsion produced by magnets

Male reproductive system: produces sperms for reproduction

Malleable: can be beaten into sheets

Maltase: an enzyme that breaks down starch into simpler maltose

Mammal: a warm-blooded vertebrate with hair or fur covering its body. It feeds its young with milk from the female's mammary glands. E.g. monkeys and cows

Mass: the amount of matter in a substance

Matter: anything that has mass or occupies space

Measuring balance: an instrument that measures mass

Measuring instrument: instrument that measures a physical property

Melting: occurs when a solid changes into a liquid

Melting point: the temperature at which the substance changes from solid to liquid

Menstruation: the discharge of disintegrated uterus lining together with the unfertilised egg and blood through the vagina; also called period

Menstrual cycle: a cycle of ovulation and menstruation that usually takes about 28 days

Metre: SI unit for length

Metre rule: an instrument that measures length accurate to 0.1 cm

Microfiltration: a process in which water is passed through membranes to remove solids and bacteria

Mixture: consists of two or more substances that are not joined together chemically

Molecule: made up of two or more atoms of the same kind or of different kinds chemically combined together. Molecules in an element consist of a fixed number of one kind of atom chemically combined together. Molecules in a compound consist of a fixed number of two or more different kinds of atoms chemically combined.

Multicellular: made up of more than one cell

Muscular system: enables movement

N

Nervous system: controls actions and coordinates working of the body. It enables us to respond to stimuli.

Neutrons: a particle that is not charged

NEWater: high grade water that is purified from used water in Singapore

Nucleus: part of the cell that controls all the chemical reactions that take place in the cell

O

Oesophagus (gullet): a narrow tube with strong muscles in its walls. The muscles contract and relax, producing a wave-like pattern that pushes the food along the oesophagus to the stomach.

Opaque: a physical property of a substance that stops light from passing through it

Organ: a group of different tissues working together to carry out one or more bodily functions. E.g. heart and stomach

Organism: a living thing that needs oxygen, food and water to survive

Osmosis: the net movement of water molecules through a partially permeable membrane from a region of higher water concentration to a region of lower water concentration

Ovary: the female organ which produces eggs and female sex hormones

Oviduct (Fallopian tube): part of the female reproductive system; contains muscles which contract rhythmically to produce rippling movements to carry a mature egg to the uterus

Ovulation: the release of a mature egg from an ovary

Ovum (plural – ova): the female sex cell; egg

P

Pancreas: an organ that releases insulin to aid the digestion of sugar

Pancreatic duct: a tube that joins the pancreas to the small intestines

Paper chromatography: used to separate and identify the different coloured components in mixtures such as dyes and inks

Partially permeable membrane: a membrane which allows only certain substances to pass through

Particulate: referring to particles

Penis: the male sex organ which ejects sperms

Periodic table: a table that arranges elements according to their chemical properties systematically

Permanent contraceptive methods: those which prevent their users from having any more children once these methods have been applied

Phloem: transport tubes found in flowering plants that carry food made in the leaves to all other parts of the plant

Physical digestion: breaking down of big particles of food into smaller particles without changing the chemical structure of the food molecules

Physical quantity: something that can be observed and measured

Plant transport system: transports substances around the plant

Plasma: a yellow-coloured component of the blood

Platelets: blood cells that help to stop bleeding

Pollution: the release of harmful substances into the environment

Pre-marital sex: sexual intercourse before getting married

Process skills: a major element of science as an inquiry

Products of science: information from experiments and ideas such as theories and laws

Protease: enzyme that breaks down protein into amino acids in the stomach and small intestine

Protein: a complex structure made up of amino acids

Protons: positively charged particles

Puberty: the stage of growth in a young human being when his or her reproductive organs start to produce sex hormones and sex cells

R

Red blood cells: cells that carry the oxygen

Rate: ratio between two physical quantities

Rectum: used to store faeces

Reptile: a cold-blooded vertebrate with dry, scaly skin and which reproduces by laying eggs on land. E.g. snakes and crocodiles

Residue: the insoluble solid particles trapped in the filter during filtration

Respiratory system: enables the exchange of gases in and out of the body

Reverse osmosis: a method of desalination or purifying seawater by forcing the seawater through a filter membrane under high pressure to sift out the salt and waste particles

S

Salivary glands: an organ that releases saliva containing maltase for the partial digestion of starch in our mouth

Saturated solution: containing a large amount of solute

Scientific method: a systematic method used by scientists to conduct an experiment

Scrotum: a sac which holds the testis outside the body where it can be kept cool

Second: SI unit for time

Sex gland: an organ that produces sex hormones

Sex hormones: chemicals that are released with the onset of puberty

Sexual reproduction: a process where new organisms are reproduced with the involvement of two individuals of the opposite sex

Sexually transmitted infection (STI): an infection which is passed from one infected person to another during sexual intercourse or sexual contact

SI unit: a system of units used for measurements. SI stands for Système International d'Unités in French

Skeletal system: supports our body, protects the vital organs and enables movement

Small intestines: a part of the digestive system where the digestion of food is completed and simple food molecules are absorbed in the body

Solubility: the maximum amount of a substance that can dissolve in a given amount of a solvent at a particular temperature

Solute: the substance that dissolves in a solution

Solution: a homogeneous mixture that is made up of solute(s) dissolving in a solvent

Solvent: the substance that dissolves the solute in a solution

Speed: the distance travelled per unit time. SI unit – metres per second (m/s)

Sperm: the male sex cell produced in the testis

Sperm duct (vas deferens): a long tube which carries the sperms from the coiled tube to the urethra

Spermicides: chemicals that kill sperms

Square metre: SI unit of area

Starch: complex food molecule found in bread, rice, potato

Starch grains: starch stored in plant cells

Sterilisation: the removal of a person's reproductive capabilities permanently

Stomach: an organ that physically and chemically digests food after it passes through the oesophagus

Stopwatch: an instrument that measures an interval of time

Strength: the ability of a material to support a heavy load without breaking or tearing

Suspension: a mixture containing solid particles suspended in a liquid or a gas

Syphilis: a sexually transmitted disease caused by spiral bacteria. The symptoms of the primary stage of syphilis include painless sores and non-itchy rash. In the later stages of the disease, the victim may develop deformed joints, become paralysed or insane and may even die.

System: a group of organs working together to perform a particular function. E.g. the reproductive system

T

Taxonomic group: the ranking of an organism within a hierarchical classification

Technology: an application of scientific knowledge for the use and benefit of mankind

Temperature: a measure of the degree of hotness

Temporary contraceptive methods: those which allow couples to have children as and when the couples stop using these methods

Testis (plural - testes): the male reproductive organ which produces sperms and male sex hormones

Thermal conductivity: a measure of how readily heat flows through a material

Thermal conductor: a material that allows heat to pass through readily

Thermal insulator: a material that does not allow heat to pass through readily

Time: an instant or interval

Tissue: cells of the same type arranged in groups or layers

Tissue fluid: blood plasma that leaks out from capillary walls and fills up the spaces between the cells close to the capillaries

Tongue: an organ that physically and chemically digests food before it passes through the oesophagus

U

Unicellular: made up of only one cell

Universal Indicator: a mixture of different indicators that have different colours across the entire pH range

Universal solvent: a solvent that can dissolve a large variety of substances, also known as water

Urethra: a tube in the male reproductive system which carries the sperms from the sperm duct through the penis to the outside of the body

Uterus: a pear-shaped structure which has thick walls of muscles in the female reproductive system; also called womb

UV irradiation: a process that kills bacteria and micro-organisms by the action of ultra-violet (UV) rays

V

Vacuole: a space in the cytoplasm of a cell containing air, liquid or food particles. In plant cells, the vacuole is filled with cell sap.

Vagina: the female sex organ

Vasectomy: male sterilisation which involves the removal of a section of the sperm duct

Vernier calipers: an instrument that measures length accurate to 0.01 cm

Vertebrate: an animal with a backbone. E.g. fish and mammals

Volume: the amount of space occupied by matter

W

White blood cells: cells that provide the body with immunity against infections

X

Xylem: transports water and mineral salts in a plant

Z

Zero error: a non-zero reading shown on a scale when nothing is being measured

Index

S

Scientific method 7-8
Scrotum 217
Separation technique
    desalination 102
    distillation 100, 102
    evaporation 95, 98-99
    filtration 95, 97, 103
    paper chromatography 101
    reverse osmosis 102-103
    magnetic attraction 95-96
Sexual reproduction 212, 221
Sexually transmitted infection (STI) 226-228
SI unit
    cubic metre 33, 56
    metre 26
    square metre 31
Small intestine 200, 206
Solubility 114-115
Solution
    acid 85, 108, 116-124
    alkali 108, 116, 119-124
    aqueous solution 109, 116, 118
    dilute solution 109
    homogenous solution110, 113
    saturated solution 109
    solute 98-99, 108-111, 113-115
    solvent 98-101, 108-111, 114-115
Speed
    average speed 57-58
Sperm
    sperm duct (vas deferens) 217, 222, 224
Starch
    starch grain 149
Sterilisation 224
Stomach 200, 203-206
Strength 66, 71
Suspension 108, 112-113, 119
Syphilis 227-228
System
    muscular system 155
    blood circulatory system 154, 192
    digestive system 154
    female reproductive system 155, 216, 218
    male reproductive system 155, 217
    nervous system 154
    plant transport system 191
    respiratory system 154
    skeletal system 155

T

Technology 3, 16-20
Testis (plural - testes) 217
Thermal
    thermal conductivity 66, 69, 71
    thermal conductor 69
    thermal insulator 69
Tissue 193, 198
Tongue 203-204
Transport system
    phloem 191
    plasma 192-193
    platelet 192
    red blood cell 150, 157, 189, 192-193
    tissue fluid 193, 198
    white blood cell 192
    xylem 191

U

Universal solvent 109
Urethra 217, 222, 224
Uterus 218-222, 224-225
UV irradiation 103

V

Vagina 217-220
Vernier calipers
    zero error 30-31
Volume 33-35